Latin

FOR COMMON ENTRANCE

13+
LEVEL 2

Exam Practice Questions

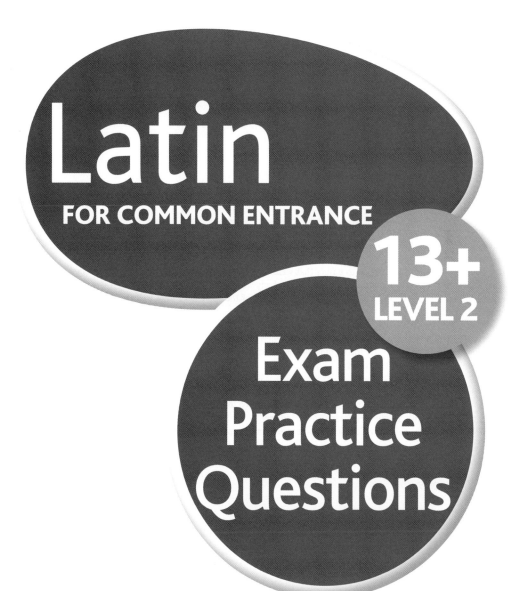

Latin

FOR COMMON ENTRANCE

13+
LEVEL 2

Exam Practice Questions

R.C. Bass

GALORE PARK

AN HACHETTE UK COMPANY

About the author

Bob Bass taught at prep schools in Somerset, Kenya and Sussex before moving in 1987 to Orwell Park, Ipswich, where he is Head of Classics and Senior Master. He has served on the editorial board of the *Journal of Classics Teaching* and on the Council of the Joint Association of Classical Teachers. For 12 years he edited the SATIPS Classics Broadsheet, and has been IAPS' Subject Leader and then Subject Adviser in Classics. He is the Chief Setter of ISEB's Common Entrance and Common Academic Scholarship Latin papers, proof-reader for their Greek papers, and an IGCSE examiner. He is the author of various Latin and Greek resources targeted at young learners.

Every effort has been made to trace all copyright holders, but if any have been inadvertently overlooked, the Publishers will be pleased to make the necessary arrangements at the first opportunity.

Although every effort has been made to ensure that website addresses are correct at time of going to press, Galore Park cannot be held responsible for the content of any website mentioned in this book. It is sometimes possible to find a relocated web page by typing in the address of the home page for a website in the URL window of your browser.

Hachette UK's policy is to use papers that are natural, renewable and recyclable products and made from wood grown in sustainable forests. The logging and manufacturing processes are expected to conform to the environmental regulations of the country of origin.

Orders: please contact Bookpoint Ltd, 130 Milton Park, Abingdon, Oxon OX14 4SB. Telephone: (44) 01235 827720. Fax: (44) 01235 400454. Email education@bookpoint.co.uk Lines are open from 9 a.m. to 5 p.m., Monday to Saturday, with a 24-hour message answering service. Visit our website at www.galorepark.co.uk for details of other revision guides for Common Entrance, examination papers and Galore Park publications.

ISBN: 978 1 4718 5347 0

© Robert C. Bass 2015

First published in 2015 by
Galore Park Publishing Ltd,
An Hachette UK Company
Carmelite House
50 Victoria Embankment
London EC4Y 0DZ
www.galorepark.co.uk

Impression number   10 9 8 7 6 5 4 3 2 1

Year   2019 2018 2017 2016 2015

Typeset in India

Printed and bound by CPI Group (UK) Ltd, Croydon, CR0 4YY

A catalogue record for this title is available from the British Library.

Contents

Introduction

This collection of practice exercises, previously published as Latin Practice Exercises Level 2, is designed to provide material for pupils in their second year of learning Latin, particularly those preparing for the ISEB Common Entrance examination at Level 2. Companion volumes are available for Levels 1 and 3.

It provides extensive material for translation, both into and out of Latin, giving pupils the opportunity to revise or consolidate skills learnt in those courses.

The vocabulary, grammar and syntax are deliberately geared to the Level 2 syllabus for Common Entrance. Five words from the Level 3 syllabus are included, however:

adeo = I go towards; **alius** = other; **aut** = either; **relinquo** = I leave; **telum** = spear.

It will not hurt to learn these words as and when they occur in the course.

An answer book, including mark schemes for the exercises, is available separately. For a full list of resources available visit www.galorepark.co.uk

A sequence of 12 test papers, *The Story of Perseus*, is included at the end of the book. It is suggested that these are not attempted before pupils have completed Chapter 3.

Nicholas Oulton
Series Editor

→ The syllabus and your exams

For Common Entrance Latin, you will sit an exam lasting one hour. You will choose one of the three levels, Level 1, Level 2 or Level 3, as agreed with your teacher.

The format of each level is the same, but the material gets harder. In each level, there are four questions worth a total of 75 marks, as follows:

Question 1 (15 marks)

A short passage of Latin will be set, on which you will be asked to answer eight to ten questions, testing your understanding of the passage. You will not be expected to write a translation of the passage, but clearly you need to have translated it in your head, in order to answer the questions.

Question 2 (30 marks)

Another, slightly longer passage will be set, continuing the story from the passage in Question 1. You will be asked to translate this passage, writing your translation on alternate lines.

Question 3 (20 marks)

Another short passage of Latin will be set, continuing the story from the earlier two passages. Questions will be set, testing your knowledge of Latin grammar and how the language works. You will not be asked to translate this passage, but again you will find it difficult to answer the questions unless you have translated it for yourself.

The questions will fall into the following types:

- From the passage give, in Latin, one example of: (an adjective, a preposition followed by the accusative, a noun in the genitive, a verb in the imperfect tense, etc.)

- **erat** (line 2). In which tense is this verb? What is the 1st person singular of the present tense of this verb?

- **pueros** (line 4). In which case is this noun? Why is this case used?

- **vocaverunt** (line 5). What does this word mean? What is the connection between **vocaverunt** and the English word *vocation*?

- **necat** (line 5) means *he kills*. How would you say in Latin *he was killing* (imperfect tense)?

And last but not least:

- Using the vocabulary given, translate the following two short sentences into Latin.

Most candidates lose the majority of their marks on Question 3 by falling into the trap of thinking they do not need to translate the passage. They simply guess the answers. To answer a question such as 'in which case is the word **templum** in line 3?', you have to have translated the sentence in which the word **templum** is. Otherwise you will simply be guessing, particularly with a word such as **templum**, which could be any of nominative, vocative or accusative singular.

Question 4 (10 marks)

You will be set eight questions on four areas: Roman domestic life; the city of Rome; the army and Roman Britain; and Greek mythology. Each question will have two parts, part (i) and part (ii). You select **one** question, and answer both parts of it. Examples are given below:

The city of Rome

(c) (i) Tell the story of Cloelia.

(ii) Which elements of this story would the Romans have found particularly admirable? Explain your answer.

Greek mythology

(h) (i) Tell the story of Odysseus' encounter with the Cyclops.

(ii) Describe two qualities which Odysseus displayed in this encounter.

These are two of the eight questions that might have been set, labelled (a) to (h). If you had chosen to do the one labelled (c) above, you would have done both part (i) and part (ii) of that question.

→ Tips on revising

For Common Entrance Latin, you will sit an exam lasting one hour. You will choose one of the three levels, Level 1, Level 2 or Level 3, as agreed with your teacher.

Get the best out of your brain

- Give your brain plenty of oxygen by exercising. You can only revise effectively if you feel fit and well.

- Eat healthy food while you are revising. Your brain works better when you give it good fuel.

- Think positively. Give your brain positive messages so that it will want to study.

- Keep calm. If your brain is stressed, it will not operate effectively.

- Take regular breaks during your study time.

- Get enough sleep. Your brain will carry on sorting out what you have revised while you sleep.

Get the most from your revision

- Don't work for hours without a break. Revise for 20–30 minutes, then take a five-minute break.

- Do good things in your breaks: listen to your favourite music, eat healthy food, drink some water, do some exercise or juggle. Don't read a book, watch TV or play on the computer; it will conflict with what your brain is trying to learn.

- When you go back to your revision, review what you have just learnt.

- Regularly review the material you have learnt.

Get motivated

- Set yourself some goals and promise yourself a treat when the exams are over.

- Make the most of all the expertise and talent available to you at school and at home. If you don't understand something, ask your teacher to explain.

- Get organised. Find a quiet place to revise and make sure you have all the equipment you need.

- Use year and weekly planners to help you organise your time so that you revise all subjects equally. (Available for download from www.galorepark.co.uk)

- Use topic and subject checklists to help you keep on top of what you are revising. (Available for download from www.galorepark.co.uk)

Know what to expect in the exam

- Use past papers to familiarise yourself with the format of the exam.

- Make sure you understand the language examiners use.

Before the exam

- Have all your equipment and pens ready the night before.

- Make sure you are at your best by getting a good night's sleep before the exam.

- Have a good breakfast in the morning.

- Take some water into the exam if you are allowed.

- Think positively and keep calm.

During the exam

- Have a watch on your desk. Work out how much time you need to allocate to each question and try to stick to it.

- Make sure you read and understand the instructions on the front of the exam paper.

- Allow some time at the start to read and consider the questions carefully before writing anything.

- Read every question at least twice. Don't rush into answering before you have a chance to think about it.

1

→ Revision

Exercise 1.1

Translate the following into English:

1 fuisti.

2 amaverunt.

3 currunt.

4 videmus.

5 scribebas.

6 pugno.

7 respondet.

8 respondit.

9 manebamus.

10 clamant.

1 mark for each question. Total: 10

Exercise 1.2

Translate the following into English:

1 ducis.

2 dicis.

3 luserunt.

4 mittimus.

5 movimus.

6 discessistis.

7 oppugnabas.

8 ostenditis.

9 paravit.

10 posui.

1 mark for each question. Total: 10

Exercise 1.3

Translate the following into English:

1 videmus.

2 superaverunt.

3 eratis.

4 portabatis.

5 audiunt.

6 necavit.

7 necant.

8 movit.

9 iussit.

10 dat.

1 mark for each question. Total: 10

Exercise 1.4

Translate the following into English:

1 constituerunt.

2 cepit.

3 cupiebam.

4 ducebat.

5 iecimus.

6 laudatis.

7 steterunt.

8 portavisti.

9 mittis.

10 festinabamus.

1 mark for each question. Total: 10

Exercise 1.5

Translate the following into English:

1 celeriter currebamus.

2 fortiter pugnabat.

3 diu navigaverunt.

4 numquam ludo.

5 bene scribis.

6 saepe flebant.

7 diu dormivi.

8 tandem discesserunt.

9 subito intravit.

10 semper bibit.

2 marks for each question. Total: 20

Exercise 1.6

Translate the following into English:

1 Romani magnum oppidum aedificaverunt. (4)

2 nauta pericula non timebat. (4)

3 turba feminarum in via stabat. (5)

4 multa verba dixisti. (3)

5 Romani multa templa deleverunt. (4)

Total: 20

Exercise 1.7

Translate the following into English:

1 oppidum novum muros altos habet. (5)

2 multi nautae celeriter appropinquant. (4)

3 hodie laboro. heri tamen nihil feci. (6)

4 Romani multa scuta portabant. (4)

5 multi viri boni in proelio pugnaverunt. (6)

Total: 25

Exercise 1.8

Translate the following into English:

1 nuntii in templum sacrum festinaverunt.

2 olim multi Romani clari erant.

3 dominus malus servum miserum necavit.

4 ancillae pulchrae cibum bonum parabant.

5 pueri mali magistros numquam audiunt.

5 marks for each question. Total: 25

Exercise 1.9

Translate the following into English:

1 magister puerum verbis iratis terruit.

2 gladiis et scutis semper pugnamus.

3 dominus multam pecuniam servo dedit.

4 parvum puerum hasta mea necavi.

5 poeta clarus librum bonum legebat.

5 marks for each question. Total: 25

Exercise 1.10

Translate the following into English:

1 verba nautarum mala erant. (4)

2 turbae servorum veniunt. (3)

3 muri templi alti et validi sunt. (6)

4 amicus pueri cantabat. (3)

5 verba magistri numquam audimus. (4)

Total: 20

Exercise 1.11

Translate the following into English:

1 ludere amant. (2)

2 servus pugnare cupiebat. (3)

3 dominus servum laborare iussit. (4)

4 laborare numquam cupio. (3)

5 nuntius currere constituit. (3)

Total: 15

Chapter 1

Exercise 1.12

Translate the following into English:

1 lente ambulate, pueri!

2 librum scribe, poeta!

3 equos movete, agricolae!

4 vinum bibe, amice!

5 arma relinquite, nautae!

3 marks for each question. Total: 15

Exercise 1.13

Translate the following into English:

1 puer in via stabat.

2 servi contra dominum pugnaverunt.

3 in magno periculo sumus.

4 nuntius per viam cucurrit.

5 puella cum amicis ludit.

4 marks for each question. Total: 20

Exercise 1.14

Translate the following into English:

1 agricolane caelum diu spectabat? (4)

2 magisterne verba mala dixit? (4)

3 servine murum oppugnant? (3)

4 puerine scuta habent? (3)

5 dominusne multos servos et ancillas habebat? (6)

Total: 20

Exercise 1.15

Give the translation, person, number, tense and the 1st person singular of the present tense of the following verbs:

Example					
sunt.	They are	3rd person	Plural	Present	sum

1 rident.

2 oppugnabat.

3 ponebamus.

4 dedistis.

5 steterunt.

6 laboraverunt.

7 constituunt.

8 cucurristis.

9 scripserunt.

10 parabamus.

5 marks for each question. Total: 50

Exercise 1.16

Give the translation, person, number, tense and the 1st person singular of the present tense of the following verbs:

1 veniunt.

2 erat.

3 portabas.

4 necas.

5 biberunt.

6 dormiebas.

7 iussit.

8 monet.

9 cepisti.

10 dicebant.

5 marks for each question. Total: 50

Exercise 1.17

Give and translate the following verb parts:

1 The 1st person singular, imperfect tense of **amo**.

2 The 2nd person plural, present tense of **sum**.

3 The 2nd person singular, perfect tense of **curro**.

4 The 3rd person plural, perfect tense of **pono**.

5 The 1st person plural, imperfect tense of **dormio**.

2 marks for each question. Total: 10

Exercise 1.18

Give and translate the following verb parts:

1 The 3rd person singular, present tense of **video**.

2 The 2nd person plural, imperfect tense of **bibo**.

3 The 1st person plural, perfect tense of **dico**.

4 The 3rd person plural, present tense of **festino**.

5 The 2nd person singular, perfect tense of **moneo**.

2 marks for each question. Total: 10

Exercise 1.19

Give and translate the following verb parts:

1 The 3rd person singular, perfect tense of **sum**.

2 The 1st person singular, imperfect tense of **teneo**.

3 The 2nd person singular, present tense of **rego**.

4 The 3rd person singular, present tense of **rideo**.

5 The 2nd person singular, imperfect tense of **facio**.

2 marks for each question. Total: 10

Exercise 1.20

Put into the plural and translate your answer:

1 oppidum oppugno.

2 equum habebas.

3 puellam spectavit.

4 periculum timet.

5 terram regebat.

2 + 2 marks for each question. Total: 20

Exercise 1.21

Put into the plural and translate your answer:

1 puella puerum amat.

2 magister librum iacit.

3 puer scutum habet.

4 ancilla cibum parat.

5 nauta murum aedificat.

3 + 3 marks for each question. Total: 30

Exercise 1.22

Put into the plural and translate your answer:

1 agricola hastam portabat.

2 vir periculum timebat.

3 dominus servum punivit.

4 puer magistrum audivit.

5 poeta librum scripsit.

3 + 3 marks for each question. Total: 30

Exercise 1.23

Put into the singular and translate your answer:

1 ancillas habebamus.

2 gladios portatis.

3 deas viderunt.

4 pericula timebatis.

5 viros laudavimus.

2 + 2 marks for each question. Total: 20

Exercise 1.24

Put into the singular and translate your answer:

1 servi templa aedificaverunt.

2 nautae scuta portabant.

3 pueri mali erant.

4 reginae terras regunt.

5 servi dominos necaverunt.

3 + 3 marks for each question. Total: 30

Exercise 1.25

Put into the singular and translate your answer:

1 nautae feminas non timebant.

2 agricolae agros amant.

3 oppida muros habebant.

4 magistri pueros puniebant.

5 puellae deos laudabant.

3 + 3 marks for each question. Total: 30

Exercise 2.1

Translate the following passage. Line numbers are given on the left. New words are underlined in the text and their meanings given in the margin.

Discord gatecrashes the wedding party of Peleus and the goddess Thetis

1 olim in <u>monte Olympo</u> dei et deae <u>festum</u>
<u>celebrabant</u>. cibum consumebant et vinum
bibebant. <u>festum</u> <u>celebrabant</u> quod Peleus
Thetim in <u>matrimonium ducebat</u>. Thetis dea
5 erat. Peleus vir <u>mortalis</u> erat. dei deae<u>que</u> laeti
erant. ridebant. subito tamen Discordia, dea
mala, intravit. <u>ceteri</u> dei, ubi Discordiam
viderunt, non laeti erant. non iam ridebant.
non ridebant quod Discordiam non amabant.
10 clamaverunt: 'quid cupis, Discordia? cur hic
stas? te non amamus. statim discede!'
Discordia <u>nuntiavit</u>: 'me audite, dei! me audite,
deae! <u>donum</u> habeo. <u>donum</u> pulchrum habeo.
hic est.' deinde Discordia <u>pomum</u> <u>deposuit</u>.
15 risit discessit<u>que</u>. dei deae<u>que</u> ad <u>pomum</u>
<u>appropinquaverunt</u>. <u>pomum</u> spectaverunt.

monte Olympo = Mount
Olympus
festum celebro, -are,
-avi (1) = I hold a
celebration
Thetim = accusative case
of Thetis (a sea nymph,
Greek form)
in matrimonium duco
(3) = I marry
mortalis = mortal
-que = and (before the
word it is attached to)
ceteri = the rest of
nuntio, -are, -avi (1) =
I announce
donum, -i, n. = gift
pomum, -i, n. = apple
deposuit = put down
appropinquo, -are, -avi
(1) = I approach

Total: 95

Exercise 2.2

1 From the passage give, in Latin, one example of each of the following:

(a) a verb in the imperfect tense. (1)

(b) a verb in the perfect tense. (1)

(c) a part of the verb 'to be'. (1)

(d) an imperative. (1)

(e) a personal pronoun. (1)

2 Discordia (line 10). In which case is this noun? (1)

3 risit (line 15). Give the person, number and tense of this verb.
Give the 1st person singular of the present tense of this verb. (4)

Total: 10

➜ Translating 'and' into Latin

There are two ways of writing 'and' in Latin, as shown in the examples below:

Examples

1 the word et is used between two words

Marcus et Sextus.

Marcus and Sextus.

2 the ending –que is added to the end of the second word

pueri puellaeque.

Boys and girls.

Exercise 2.3

Read these instructions carefully. For each question write out:

(a) the same Latin sentence with the et replaced by a -que in the correct place;

(b) an English translation of the Latin sentence.

Example

Marcus et Sextus sunt laeti.

(a) Marcus Sextusque sunt laeti.

(b) Marcus and Sextus are happy.

1 pueri semper currunt et clamant.   (1 + 5)

2 Iulia et Valeria sunt puellae.   (1 + 5)

3 agricolae et nautae veniunt.   (1 + 4)

4 currimus et ludimus.   (1 + 3)

5 amici rident et ludunt.   (1 + 4)

6 servus est fessus et laetus.   (1 + 5)

7 puer cibum et aquam habet.   (1 + 5)

8 contra Romanos et Graecos pugnamus.   (1 + 5)

9 agricolae hastas et sagittas habent.   (1 + 5)

10 pueri intrant et laborant.   (1 + 4)

Total: 55

Exercise 2.4

Translate the following into English:

1 Marcus Sextusque sunt pueri.   (5)

2 rideo ludoque.   (3)

3 puer puellaque currunt.   (4)

4 servus timet fugitque.   (4)

5 pueri currunt luduntque.   (4)

6 servi dominique veniunt. (4)

7 magister pueros puellasque monet. (5)

8 dominus intrat servumque punit. (5)

9 puella intrat amicumque videt. (5)

10 pueri puellaeque rident luduntque. (6)

Total: 45

Exercise 2.5

Translate the following into English:

1 Romulus Remusque Romani erant. (5)

2 semper ridemus ludimusque. (4)

3 Valeria Aureliaque puellae Romanae sunt. (6)

4 magister Sextum Marcumque punit. (5)

5 Sextus Marcusque magistrum audiunt. (5)

6 magister puerum puellamque spectabat. (5)

7 puer agricolas nautasque timebat. (5)

8 servi cibum aquamque habebant. (5)

9 servi fessi miserique erant. (5)

10 templum sacrum pulchrumque erat. (5)

Total: 50

Exercise 2.6

Translate the following into English:

1 terruisti.

2 rogaverunt.

3 deleverunt.

4 misimus.

5 vidit.

6 audivisti.

7 constituerunt.

8 clamavistis.

9 reximus.

10 venit.

1 mark for each question. Total: 10

Exercise 2.7

Translate the following into English:

1 dixit.

2 iussit.

3 cucurrimus.

4 nuntiavit.

5 fecisti.

6 mansimus.

7 cepistis.

8 appropinquaverunt.

9 bibi.

10 fuit.

1 mark for each question. Total: 10

Exercise 2.8

Translate the following into Latin:

1 I have feared.

2 We loved.

3 They have been.

4 You (sing.) saw.

5 You (pl.) gave.

6 He heard.

7 We led.

8 She laughed.

9 I ruled.

10 They stood.

1 mark for each question. Total: 10

Exercise 2.9

Translate the following into Latin:

1 We moved.

2 I announced.

3 You (pl.) put.

4 We have been.

5 He decided.

6 I took.

7 You (sing.) wrote.

8 They threw.

9 We approached.

10 They departed.

1 mark for each question. Total: 10

Exercise 2.10

Put into the plural and translate your answer:

1	appropinquabam.	(1 + 1)
2	discipulus laborat.	(2 + 2)
3	servus pugnabat.	(2 + 2)
4	puer bonus est.	(3 + 3)
5	nauta navigavit.	(2 + 2)

Total: 20

Exercise 2.11

Put into the singular and translate your answer:

1	libri boni sunt.	(3 + 3)
2	gladios portabatis.	(2 + 2)
3	bella timemus.	(2 + 2)
4	nautae magnas hastas iecerunt.	(4 + 4)
5	servi muros altos aedificabant.	(4 + 4)

Total: 30

Chapter 2

Exercise 2.12

Give and translate the following verb parts:

1 The 1st person singular, imperfect tense of **nuntio**.

2 The 2nd person plural, perfect tense of **navigo**.

3 The 3rd person singular, present tense of **aedifico**.

4 The 1st person singular, perfect tense of **sto**.

5 The 3rd person plural, perfect tense of **sum**.

2 marks for each question. Total: 10

Exercise 2.13

Put into the singular, and translate your answer:

1 puellae non cantant. (2 + 3)

2 dona pulchra sunt. (3 + 3)

3 servi muros aedificabant. (3 + 3)

4 pueri scuta portaverunt. (3 + 3)

5 discipuli magistros saepe timent. (3 + 4)

Total: 30

Exercise 2.14

Give the translation, person, number, tense and the 1st person singular of the present tense of these verbs:

1 nuntiavit.

2 appropinquabant.

3 iecisti.

4 oppugnamus.

5 iussit.

5 marks for each question. Total: 25

Exercise 2.15

Keeping the same person and number, put the following verbs into the imperfect tense and translate your answer:

1 appropinquaverunt.

2 nuntiavit.

3 navigavi.

4 oppugnavisti.

5 iussit.

6 iusserunt.

7 superavimus.

8 stetit.

9 deleverunt.

10 dedimus.

2 marks for each question. Total: 20

Exercise 3.1

Translate the following passage. Line numbers are given on the left. New words are underlined in the text and their meanings given in the margin.

On Mount Olympus the three goddesses Juno, Athena and Venus argue over the golden apple

1 dei deaeque in <u>monte</u> Olympo erant. <u>pomum</u>
spectabant. <u>pomum</u> pulchrum erat. <u>pomum</u>
<u>aureum</u> erat. <u>haec</u> verba in <u>pomo</u> erant: '<u>hoc</u>
<u>pomum</u> <u>aureum</u> feminae <u>pulcherrimae</u> est.'
5 Iuno regina deorum erat. <u>et</u> <u>soror</u> <u>et</u> <u>uxor</u>
<u>Iovis</u> erat. dea Iuno <u>pomum</u> spectavit. verba
legit. 'ego dea <u>pulcherrima</u> sum,' clamavit.
'<u>pomum</u> igitur meum est.' dea Athena <u>pomum</u>
spectavit. verba legit. '<u>erras</u>, Iuno,' clamavit.
10 '<u>pomum</u> meum est. <u>pomum</u> meum est quod
ego <u>pulcherrima</u> sum.' dea Venus <u>pomum</u>
spectavit. verba legit. '<u>erratis</u>, deae. ego
<u>pulcherrima</u> sum. <u>pomum</u> igitur meum est.
<u>pomum</u> <u>mihi tradite</u>!' sic tres deae de <u>pomo</u>
15 <u>aureo</u> <u>disputabant</u>. <u>omnes</u> <u>pomum</u> <u>aureum</u>
habere cupiebant. ad <u>Iovem</u> appropinquare
igitur constituerunt. <u>Iuppiter</u> <u>et</u> <u>pater</u> <u>et</u> <u>rex</u>
deorum erat.

mons, montis, m. = mountain
pomum, -i, n. = apple
aureus, -a, -um = golden
haec = these
hoc = this
pulcherrimus, -a, -um = the most beautiful
et…et… = both… and…
soror = sister
uxor = wife
Iuppiter, Iovis, m. = Jupiter
erro, -are, -avi (1) = I am wrong

mihi tradite! = hand over to me!
disputo, -are, -avi (1) = I argue
omnes, = (they) all
pater = father
rex = king

Total: 110

Exercise 3.2

1 From the passage give, in Latin, one example of each of the following:

(a) an imperative. (1)

(b) an infinitive. (1)

2 pomo (line 3). In which case is this noun? Why is this case used? (2)

3 deorum (line 5). Give the case and gender of this noun. (2)

4 erat (line 6). Give the person, number and tense of this verb. Give the 1st person singular of the present tense of this verb. (4)

Total: 10

Exercise 3.3

Give the correct form of the following nouns:

1 The nominative plural of **pater, patris**, m.

2 The genitive singular of **uxor, uxoris**, f.

3 The dative plural of **mons, montis**, m.

4 The ablative singular of **mater, matris**, f.

5 The genitive plural of **soror, sororis**, f.

6 The dative singular of **pater, patris**, m.

7 The ablative plural of **uxor, uxoris**, f.

8 The accusative singular of **soror, sororis**, f.

9 The accusative plural of **pater, patris**, m.

10 The vocative singular of **rex, regis**, m.

1 mark for each question. Total: 10

Exercise 3.4

Give the correct form of the following nouns:

1 The genitive singular of **rex, regis**, m.

2 The nominative singular of **uxor, uxoris**, f.

3 The dative singular of **mater, matris**, f.

4 The vocative singular of **pater, patris**, m.

5 The dative plural of **frater, fratris**, m.

6 The accusative singular of **mons, montis**, m.

7 The ablative singular of **soror, sororis**, f.

8 The accusative plural of **mater, matris**, f.

9 The ablative plural of **frater, fratris**, m.

10 The genitive plural of **pater, patris**, m.

1 mark for each question. Total: 10

Exercise 3.5

Translate the following into Latin:

1 Mountains (subject).

2 For the father.

3 King! (vocative).

4 Wives (object).

5 Brother (object).

6 Of the sister.

7 For the fathers.

8 Of the mountain.

9 For the king.

10 Of the kings.

1 mark for each question. Total: 10

Exercise 3.6

Translate the following into Latin:

1 By the mountains.

2 To the sister.

3 Brothers! (vocative).

4 Of the wives.

5 For the wife.

6 Sister (object).

7 Mothers (object).

8 To the fathers.

9 For the brothers.

10 Mothers (subject).

1 mark for each question. Total: 10

Exercise 3.7

Translate the following into English:

1 montem vidi. (2)

2 pater currit. (2)

3 uxorem meam amo. (3)

4 rex regit. (2)

5 matrem amamus. (2)

6 fratrem et sororem habeo. (4)

7 rex sororem pulchram habet. (4)

8 multos montes vidimus. (3)

9 ad montem altum appropinquabamus. (4)

10 uxor mea iam venit. (4)

Total: 30

Exercise 3.8

Translate the following into English:

1 Marcus frater Aureliae est. (4)

2 Aurelia soror Marci est. (4)

3 puella cibum patri parabat. (4)

4 puella sororem non amat. (4)

5 servi ad montem festinant. (4)

6 in montibus sunt multae viae. (5)

7 rex matrem patremque amabat. (4)

8 rex uxorem pulchram habebat. (4)

9 patrem bonum habeo. (3)

10 soror mea mala est. (4)

Total: 40

Chapter 3

Exercise 3.9

Translate the following into English:

1 puer cum sorore semper pugnat. (5)

2 puella cum fratre semper pugnat. (5)

3 pater pueri iratus est. (4)

4 rex terram bene regit. (4)

5 rex pecuniam sorori dat. (4)

6 puella pecuniam regis capit. (4)

7 mater mea fratrem clarum habet. (5)

8 frater matris meae clarus erat. (5)

9 puer multa dona matri dedit. (5)

10 uxor regis pulchra est. (4)

Total: 45

Exercise 3.10

Translate the following into Latin:

1 I like high mountains. (3)

2 We saw the king. (2)

3 I have a sister. (2)

4 Mother is not coming. (3)

5 My father is good. (3)

6 My sister is sleeping. (2)

7 I love my mother. (2)

8 My mother is beautiful. (3)

9 My wife is frightened. (3)

10 We love our parents. (2)

Total: 25

Exercise 3.11

Translate the following into Latin:

1 I have a brother. (2)

2 My sister is beautiful. (3)

3 The wife was weeping. (2)

4 We saw the mountains. (2)

5 Parents like gifts. (3)

6 Mountains are tall. (3)

7 The king gave a present to his parents. (4)

8 Both brother and sister were running. (5)

9 I am handing over the money to father. (3)

10 The rest of the pupils were laughing. (3)

Total: 30

Exercise 3.12

Translate the following into Latin:

1 The king has a wife.

2 The girl praises the king.

3 Mother and father are approaching.

4 I love mother and father.

5 We are running towards the mountains.

3 marks for each question. Total: 15

Exercise 3.13

Translate the following into English:

1 et Marcus et Sextus pueri Romani sunt. (7)

2 et Valeria et Aurelia puellae Romanae sunt. (7)

3 et matrem et patrem habeo. (5)

4 soror mea et pulchra et clara est. (7)

5 magister et pueros et puellas saepe monet. (7)

6 vir magnam turbam et vidit et audivit. (7)

7 et rideo et ludo. (4)

8 Romani oppidum et hastis et sagittis oppugnaverunt. (7)

9 et mater et pater regis irati erant. (7)

10 frater meus et malus et saevus est. (7)

Total: 65

Exercise 3.14

Put into the singular and translate your answer:

1 reges festinabant. (2 + 2)

2 servi fratres habebant. (3 + 3)

3 puellae non appropinquabant. (2 + 3)

4 dona amavistis. (2 + 2)

5 viri feminas puniverunt. (3 + 3)

Total: 25

Put into the plural and translate your answer:

1   mons altus est pulcher.   (4 + 4)

2   puer patrem amat.   (3 + 3)

3   rex sororem habebat.   (3 + 3)

4   uxor bellum timet.   (3 + 3)

5   mater discessit.   (2 + 2)

Total: 30

Exercise 4.1

Translate the following passage. Line numbers are given on the left. New words are underlined in the text and their meanings given in the margin.

Jupiter passes the buck to Paris, prince of Troy

1 tres deae, ubi ad Iovem venerunt, haec verba
   dixerunt: 'Iuppiter, pomum aureum nos tres
   deae cupimus. quis est pulcherrima? lege!
   nunc lege!' Iuppiter perterritus erat. iram
5 dearum timebat. 'deae,' inquit, 'vos omnes
   pulcherrimae estis. omnes corpora pulchra
   habetis. legere non possum. iuvenem tamen
   scio, Paridem nomine. in urbe Troia habitat.
   feminas pulchras amat. ille pulcherrimam
10 leget. Paridem rogate!'
   tres deae iratae erant. Paridem tamen rogare
   constituerunt. itaque ad Paridem ierunt. iter
   longum non erat. mox igitur ad Paridem
   advenerunt. Paris, ubi lucem claram in caelo
15 vidit, timebat. deae omnia de pomo aureo
   narraverunt. 'Iuppiter nos ad te misit, Paris. te
   deam pulcherrimam legere iubet. nunc lege!'

Iuppiter, Iovis, m. = Jupiter
haec = these
pomum, -i, n. = apple
aureus, -a, -um = golden
pulcherrimus, -a, -um = the most beautiful, very beautiful
leget = will choose
nunc = now
omnes = all
corpora = bodies
possum = I am able, I can
iuvenis, -is, m. = young man
scio, -ire, -ivi (4) = I know
nomen, nominis, n. = name
urbs, urbis, f. = city
ille = he
ierunt = they went
iter, itineris, n. = journey
longus, -a, -um = long
advenio, -ire, -veni (4) = I arrive
lux, lucis, f. = light
omnia = everything
narro, -are, narravi (1) = I tell

Total: 105

Exercise 4.2

1 From the passage give, in Latin, one example of each of the following:

   (a) a preposition. (1)

   (b) an imperative. (1)

   (c) an infinitive. (1)

   (d) an adjective. (1)

2 dixerunt (line 2). Give the tense of this verb. Give the 1st person singular of the present tense of this verb. (2)

3 deae (line 5). In what case is this noun? (1)

4 habetis (line 7). Give the person, number and tense of this verb. (3)

Total: 10

→ 3rd declension nouns – neuter endings

Exercise 4.3

Give the correct form of the following nouns:

1 The nominative plural of **nomen, nominis,** n.

2 The accusative singular of **iter, itineris,** n.

3 The genitive singular of **corpus, corporis,** n.

4 The ablative plural of **flumen, fluminis,** n.

5 The dative plural of **mare, maris,** n.

6 The dative singular of **iter, itineris,** n.

7 The ablative singular of **nomen, nominis,** n.

8 The accusative plural of **corpus, corporis,** n.

9 The nominative singular of **mare, maris,** n.

10 The vocative singular of **flumen, fluminis,** n.

1 mark for each question. Total: 10

Exercise 4.4

Translate the following into Latin:

1 By name.

2 Names (object).

3 Bodies (subject).

4 To the river.

5 The sea (object).

6 By journeys.

7 Of the rivers.

8 Of the sea.

9 For the journey.

10 By rivers.

1 mark for each question. Total: 10

Exercise 4.5

Translate the following into English:

1 nauta mare non timet. (4)

2 iter longum et difficile erat. (5)

3 servi corpus portabant. (3)

4 multa itinera longa fecimus. (4)

5 aqua fluminis alta erat. (4)

6 sunt in urbe multa templa. (5)

7 oppida et urbes non amo. (5)

8 nomen regis Sextus erat. (4)

9 pater meus trans mare solus saepe navigat. (7)

10 amici itinere fessi erant. (4)

Total: 45

Exercise 4.6

Translate the following into English:

1 multa corpora in proelio vidi. (5)

2 iter iuvenum et longum et miserum erat. (7)

3 rex lucem claram in caelo vidit. (6)

4 nomen urbis Roma erat. (4)

5 puellae iuvenes pulchros saepe amant. (5)

6 pater multam pecuniam iuveni dedit. (5)

7 matrem patremque in urbe heri vidi. (6)

8 corpus nautae magnum erat. (4)

9 ad flumen mox venimus. (4)

10 itinere fessi, mox dormivimus. (4)

Total: 50

Exercise 4.7

Translate the following into Latin:

1 You (pl.) see the river. (2)

2 We are afraid of the sea. (2)

3 The sea is deep. (3)

4 My body is strong. (4)

5 The journey was long. (3)

6 I do not have a name. (3)

7 I saw many bodies. (3)

8 We do not often make journeys. (4)

9 The name of the boy is Sextus. (4)

10 I like rivers. (2)

Total: 30

Exercise 4.8

Translate the following into Latin:

1 The mother was afraid of the river. (3)

2 The king was making a long journey. (4)

3 On the journey we saw many young men. (5)

4 The sea does not frighten sailors. (4)

5 The woman had a beautiful body. (4)

Total: 20

Exercise 4.9

Translate the following into Latin:

1 The boy was standing in the river.

2 The name of the young man was Marcus.

3 We saw the rivers and the sea.

4 The water of the river was deep.

5 The waves of the sea were big.

4 marks for each question. Total: 20

Exercise 4.10

Put into the plural and translate your answer:

1 mater bona est. (3 + 3)

2 regem bonum laudo. (3 + 3)

3 fratrem habet. (2 + 2)

4 puella diu currebat. (2 + 3)

5 magister cucurrit. (2 + 2)

Total: 25

Exercise 4.11

Put into the singular and translate your answer:

1 iuvenes advenerunt.   4 corpora portatis.

2 urbes spectamus.   5 luces vidimus.

3 vina bibebamus.

2 + 2 marks for each question. Total: 20

Exercise 4.12

Give the translation, person, number, tense and 1st person singular of the present tense of the following verbs:

1 errabamus.   4 appropinquaverunt.

2 fuerunt.   5 nuntiavi.

3 tradiderunt.

5 marks for each question. Total: 25

Exercise 4.13

Give and translate the following verb parts:

1 The 1st person plural, perfect tense of **rego**.

2 The 2nd person singular, present tense of **erro**.

Chapter 4

3 The 3rd person plural, imperfect tense of sum.

4 The 1st person singular, imperfect tense of trado.

5 The 2nd person plural, perfect tense of scribo.

2 marks for each question. Total: 10

Exercise 4.14

Put into the singular and translate your answer:

1 flumina longa sunt.   (3 + 3)

2 urbes diu oppugnabatis.   (2 + 3)

3 dona amavimus.   (2 + 2)

4 pueri montes viderunt.   (3 + 3)

5 poetae narrabant.   (2 + 2)

Total: 25

Exercise 4.15

Put into the plural and translate your answer:

1 iuvenis currit.   (2 + 2)

2 iter longum est.   (3 + 3)

3 iam advenio.   (1 + 2)

4 rex urbem cepit.   (3 + 3)

5 urbs pulchra erat.   (3 + 3)

Total: 25

Exercise 4.16

Translate the following into Latin:

1 The journey was long.   (3)

2 We have seen the light.   (2)

3 He has a beautiful body.   (3)

4 The slaves attacked the city.   (3)

5 The young men threw missiles.   (3)

6 The name of the king is Marcus.   (4)

7 The man saw the girl in the city.   (5)

8 We are playing in the river.   (3)

9 Sailors are not afraid of the sea.   (4)

10 Danger does not frighten the son of the king.   (5)

Total: 35

Exercise 5.1

Translate the following passage. Line numbers are given on the left. New words are underlined in the text and their meanings given in the margin.

The goddesses cheat

1 Paris perterritus erat. respondit tamen:
 'omnes <u>pulcherrimae</u> estis, deae. nunc legere
 non <u>possum</u>. <u>cras</u> <u>redite</u>! <u>cras</u> <u>constituam</u>!'

 deae Paridi '<u>cras</u> <u>redibimus</u>,' inquiunt. iratae
5 discesserunt. <u>secreto</u> tamen Iuno ad Paridem
 appropinquavit. Paridi '<u>si</u> <u>pomum</u> <u>mihi</u> trades,'
 inquit, 'ego te virum <u>potentissimum</u> <u>faciam</u>.'
 <u>postquam</u> <u>haec</u> verba dixit, discessit. Athena
 quoque ad Paridem <u>secreto</u> appropinquavit.
10 Paridi '<u>si</u> tu me leges,' inquit, 'ego te virum
 <u>sapientissimum</u> <u>faciam</u>.' <u>postquam</u> <u>haec</u> verba
 dixit, discessit. <u>postea</u> Venus ad Paridem
 <u>secreto</u> appropinquavit. Paridi '<u>si</u> tu me leges,'
 inquit, 'ego <u>tibi</u> feminam <u>pulcherrimam</u>
15 <u>coniugem</u> <u>dabo</u>.' deinde discessit. Paris <u>solus</u>
 nunc erat.

omnes = all
pulcherrimus, -a, -um = very beautiful
possum = I am able, I can
cras = tomorrow
redite! = return!
constituam = I will decide
redibimus = we will return
secreto = in secret
si = if
pomum, -i, n. = apple
mihi = to me
potentissimus, -a, -um = the most powerful
faciam = I will make
postquam = after
haec = these
sapientissimus, -a, -um = the wisest
postea = later
tibi = to you
coniugem = as your wife
dabo = I will give
solus, -a, -um = alone

Total: 85

Exercise 5.2

1 From the passage give, in Latin, one example of each of the following:

   (a) an infinitive. (1)

   (b) an imperative. (1)

   (c) a personal pronoun. (1)

   (d) a preposition. (1)

2 dixit (line 12). Give the tense, person, number and the 1st person singular of the present tense of this verb. (4)

3 Paridem (line 12). In which case is this noun? Why is this case used? (2)

Total: 10

Future tense: 1st and 2nd conjugations

Exercise 5.3

Translate the following into English:

1 portabimus.

2 flebit.

3 sedebitis.

4 necabunt.

5 appropinquabo.

6 superabis.

7 errabit.

8 tenebunt.

9 intrabis.

10 nuntiabimus.

11 flebo.

12 dabimus.

13 narrabitis.

14 navigabis.

15 pugnabunt.

16 ridebitis.

17 videbit.

18 laborabimus.

19 cantabitis.

20 movebimus.

1 mark for each question. Total: 20

Exercise 5.4

Translate the following into English:

1 aedificabunt.

2 iubebo.

3 respondebitis.

4 stabunt.

5 pugnabimus.

6 oppugnabunt.

7 clamabit.

8 terrebitis.

9 delebunt.

10 dabitis.

11 appropinquabimus.

12 delebit.

13 manebo.

14 rogabo.

15 ridebimus.

16 videbo.

17 sedebimus

18 stabit.

19 monebitis.

20 habitabunt.

1 mark for each question. Total: 20

Exercise 5.5

Translate the following into Latin:

1 We shall stand.

2 They will carry.

3 I shall destroy.

4 He will have.

5 We shall approach.

6 You (sing.) will cry.

7 I shall overcome.

8 They will fear.

9 We shall call.

10 She will fight.

11 I shall answer.

12 You (sing.) will sit.

13 They will overcome.

14 She will laugh.

15 You (pl.) will sail.

1 mark for each question. Total: 15

Exercise 5.6

Translate the following into Latin:

1 She will remain.

2 You (pl.) will attack.

3 We shall stay.

4 You (sing.) will kill.

5 I shall hold.

6 We shall see.

7 They will watch.

8 They will cry.

9 He will frighten.

10 You (pl.) will hurry.

11 I shall move.

12 You (sing.) will approach.

13 We shall hold.

14 You (pl.) will enter.

15 They will ask.

1 mark for each question. Total: 15

→ Future tense: 3rd, 4th and mixed conjugations and sum

Exercise 5.7

Translate the following into English:

1 regemus.

2 legam.

3 advenietis.

4 curram.

5 trades.

6 constituemus.

7 eris.

8 fugiam.

9 mittent.

10 cupietis.

11 consumet.

12 erunt.

13 bibemus.

14 curremus.

15 mittet.

16 ludemus.

17 leges.

18 constituetis.

19 ludent

20 discedam

1 mark for each question. Total: 20

Exercise 5.8

Translate the following into English:

1 fugiet.

2 eritis.

3 scribemus.

4 accipient.

5 dormiet.

6 discedemus.

7 punient.

8 ero.

9 iaciam.

10 pones.

11 ostendemus.

12 dormies.

13 current.

14 capiemus.

15 erit.

16 dormiam.

17 veniam.

18 capietis.

19 accipies.

20 dicet.

1 mark for each question. Total: 20

Exercise 5.9

Translate the following into English:

1 currit.

2 curret.

3 regimus.

4 regemus.

5 festinabit.

6 festinamus.

7 est.

8 erit.

9 clamabit.

10 bibet.

11 bibit.

12 ostendent.

13 ostendunt.

14 puniet.

15 punit.

16 videmus.

17 videbimus.

18 manebunt.

19 manent.

20 erunt.

1 mark for each question. Total: 20

Exercise 5.10

Translate the following into English:

1 portabitis.

2 parant.

3 dabo.

4 delemus.

5 vocabimus.

6 delebis.

7 dormiemus.

8 narrabit.

9 habent.

10 legis.

11 dormimus.

12 intramus.

13 ridebitis.

14 leges.

15 habebo.

16 advenient.

17 fugiet.

18 fugit.

19 capiunt.

20 habebis.

1 mark for each question. Total: 20

Exercise 5.11

Translate the following into English:

1 heri servus laborabat. (3)

2 hodie servus laborat. (3)

3 cras servus fugiet. (3)

4 heri oppidum oppugnabamus. (3)

5 hodie oppidum oppugnamus. (3)

6 cras oppidum capiemus. (3)

7 heri pueri currebant. (3)

8 hodie pueri currunt. (3)

9 cras pueri current. (3)

10 heri multas puellas pulchras spectabam. (5)

11 hodie multas puellas pulchras specto. (5)

12 cras multas puellas pulchras spectabo. (5)

13 heri Romani scuta portabant. (4)

14 hodie Romani scuta portant. (4)

15 cras Romani scuta non portabunt. (5)

Total: 55

Exercise 5.12

Translate the following into Latin:

1 Many young men will arrive tomorrow. (4)

2 Help will come soon. (3)

3 My father will be making a long journey. (5)

4 The angry slaves will attack the walls. (4)

5 The boys will hurry to school. (4)

Total: 20

Exercise 5.13

Translate the following into Latin:

1 I shall drink wine tomorrow. (3)

2 Pupils will never listen to teachers. (4)

3 The young man will hurry to the town. (4)

4 The maidservant will never prepare dinner again. (5)

5 Good pupils will always work. (4)

Total: 20

Exercise 5.14

Translate the following into Latin:

1 I shall come to the city tomorrow. (4)

2 The king has a beautiful wife. (4)

3 The woman has a good husband. (4)

4 My wife was preparing a good dinner. (5)

5 We are making the journey now. (3)

Total: 20

Exercise 5.15

Translate the following into Latin:

1 The water of the river is deep. (4)

2 The wife of the king will not have money. (4)

3 We have come down from the mountain. (3)

4 You (pl.) saw the king on the journey. (4)

5 Who will be in the city tomorrow? (5)

Total: 20

Exercise 5.16

Put into the plural and translate your answer:

1 femina appropinquat. (2 + 2)

2 discipulus laborabat. (2 + 2)

3 prope flumen mansisti. (2 + 3)

4 puella donum amabat. (3 + 3)

5 iuvenis puellam vidit. (3 + 3)

Total: 25

Exercise 5.17

Put into the singular and translate your answer:

1 puellas non amamus.   (2 + 3)

2 coniuges habemus.   (2 + 2)

3 advenerunt.   (1 + 1)

4 pueri hastas portabant.   (3 + 3)

5 bene dormiverunt.   (1 + 2)

Total: 20

Exercise 6.1

Translate the following passage. Line numbers are given on the left. New words are underlined in the text and their meanings given in the margin.

Venus wins and promises Paris Helen, wife of Menelaus of Sparta

1   postero die tres deae redierunt. ante Paridem
steterunt. 'Pari, deam pulcherrimam
nunc legere debes.'

    Paris, quamquam iram dearum timebat,
5 clamavit: 'ego Venerem lego. Venus super
omnes alias dea pulcherrima est.'

    Venus, ubi verba Paridis audivit, risit. laeta erat.
Iuno et Athena, ubi verba Paridis audiverunt,
non riserunt. non laetae erant. iratae
10 discesserunt.

    Paris Venerem spectabat. 'ego te legi,' inquit.
'mulierem pulcherrimam uxorem meam cupio.
ubi est?'

    Venus Paridi respondit: 'mulier pulcherrima
15 Helena est. in Graecia cum viro
Menelao habitat. i ad Graeciam, cape
Helenam, redi ad urbem Troiam! sic mulier
pulcherrima tua erit.

postero die = on the next day
redierunt = (they) returned
ante + acc = before
pulcherrimus, -a, -um = the most beautiful
debeo, -ere, debui + infinitive (2) = I must, have to
quamquam = although
super omnes alias = above all others

mulier, mulieris, f. = woman
uxorem meam = as my wife
i = go!
redi = return!

Total: 95

Exercise 6.2

1   From the passage give, in Latin, one example of each of the following:

    (a) a verb in the perfect tense. (1)

    (b) a verb in the imperfect tense. (1)

    (c) a preposition. (1)

2   risit (line 7). Give the person, number and 1st person singular of the present tense of this verb. (3)

3   verba (line 8). Give the gender of this noun. (1)

4   Paridi (line 14). In which case is this noun? (1)

5   Graeciam (line 16). In which case is this noun? Why is this case used? (2)

Total: 10

→ eo, ire, ii/ivi = I go

Exercise 6.3

Translate the following into English:

1 redibo.

2 perierunt.

3 ibas.

4 ineunt.

5 ii.

6 ibis.

7 eo.

8 exit.

9 ibant.

10 transibunt.

11 itis.

12 rediit.

13 exibo.

14 ierunt.

15 adierunt.

1 mark for each question. Total: 15

Exercise 6.4

Translate the following into English:

1 pereo.

2 ibitis.

3 exibamus.

4 transit.

5 redii.

6 exibunt.

7 ibamus.

8 periit.

9 redibit.

10 ibat.

11 adit.

12 rediimus.

13 is.

14 exii.

15 iit.

1 mark for each question. Total: 15

Exercise 6.5

Translate the following into English:

1 transierunt.

2 ibit.

3 imus.

4 transibimus.

5 eunt.

6 peris.

7 exibat.

8 redierunt.

9 adibunt.

10 exibit.

11 transeunt.

12 redibunt.

13 redibimus.

14 pereunt.

15 ibatis.

1 mark for each question. Total: 15

Exercise 6.6

Translate the following into English:

1 periimus.

2 ibimus.

3 adeunt.

4 ibam.

5 eximus.

6 exierunt.

7 it.

8 peribo.

9 iimus.

10 rediisti.

11 transeo.

12 peribamus.

13 peribimus.

14 ibunt.

15 exibis.

1 mark for each question. Total: 15

Exercise 6.7

Translate the following into Latin:

1 We are going.

2 They went.

3 They were perishing.

4 They are crossing.

5 We will return.

6 They went in.

7 I went out.

8 I will perish.

9 We were returning.

10 Go! (sing.)

1 mark for each question. Total: 10

Exercise 6.8

Translate the following into Latin:

1 I will go out.

2 I have returned.

3 They perished.

4 He has gone out.

5 You (pl.) were going.

6 He crossed.

7 To go in.

8 They were returning.

9 We will go towards.

10 He returned.

1 mark for each question. Total: 10

Exercise 6.9

Translate the following into English:

1 heri flumen transiimus. (3)

2 hodie mare transiimus. (3)

3 ad urbem eo. (3)

4 i, puer! (2)

5 ad urbem cras adibimus. (4)

6 per viam ibamus. (3)

7 multi iuvenes perierunt. (3)

8 pueri mox redierunt. (3)

9 crasne ad urbem redibis? (4)

10 celeriter exiit. (2)

Total: 30

Exercise 6.10

Translate the following into English:

1 quis ad urbem cras ibit? (5)

2 et ego et frater ad urbem cras ibimus. (8)

3 multi servi trans flumen transierunt. (5)

4 multi iuvenes in bello perierunt. (5)

5 mater paterque ad urbem mox redibunt. (6)

6 puer ex oppido statim exiit. (5)

7 vir, ubi in templum iniit, amicum vidit. (7)

8 nauta, itinere longo fessus, ad urbem tandem adiit. (8)

9 multi servi per viam ibant. (5)

10 rex iuvenes e templo exire iussit. (6)

Total: 60

Exercise 6.11

Translate the following into Latin:

1 The young man perished in the battle. (4)

2 Both mother and father were going to the city. (7)

3 The sailor has returned from the island. (4)

4 The boys will cross the river tomorrow. (5)

5 The slaves went out of the town yesterday. (5)

Total: 25

→ Translating ubi and quamquam into good English

Hint: move the 'when' or 'although' to the beginning of the English sentence.

Examples

servus, quamquam bene laborat, multam pecuniam non habet.

The slave, although he works well, does not have much money.

Although the slave works well, he does not have much money.

Although he works well, the slave does not have much money.

vir, ubi ad urbem venit, templa spectavit.

The man, when he came to the city, looked at the temples.

When the man came to the city, he looked at the temples.

When he came to the city, the man looked at the temples.

Exercise 6.12

Translate the following into English:

1 vir, quamquam multam pecuniam habebat, non laetus erat. (8)

2 nautae, quamquam undae magnae erant, non timebant. (7)

3 rex, quamquam clarus erat, uxorem non habebat. (7)

4 quamquam iter longum non erat, iuvenes fessi erant. (8)

5 liber, quamquam longus est, bonus est. (6)

6 mulier, quamquam pulchra est, virum non habet. (7)

7 puellae, quamquam perterritae erant, in aquam celeriter inierunt. (8)

8 servus, quamquam fessus erat, bene laborabat. (6)

9 Graeci, quamquam bene pugnaverunt, Romanos non superaverunt. (7)

10 rex, quamquam Romani appropinquabant, non timebat. (6)

Total: 70

Exercise 6.13

Translate the following into English:

1 Paris, ubi lucem claram vidit, magnopere timebat. (7)

2 servi, ubi dominum viderunt, timebant. (5)

3 pueri, ubi verba magistri audiverunt, laeti erant. (7)

4 iuvenis, ubi iter longum fecit, fessus erat. (7)

5 Romani, ubi Graecos superaverunt, urbem ceperunt. (6)

6 ubi ad urbem advenimus, ad templum festinavimus. (7)

7 ubi parentes meos vidi, laetus eram. (6)

8 servi, ubi diu laboraverunt, fessi erant. (6)

9 vir, ubi donum uxori dedit, discessit. (6)

10 nautae, ubi ad insulam advenerunt, urbem spectare cupiebant. (8)

Total: 65

Exercise 6.14

Translate the following into Latin:

1 I am already crossing the deep river. (5)

2 We are going to the city. (3)

3 Many men will perish tomorrow. (4)

4 Pupils never like teachers. (3)

5 The tall woman is approaching the temple. (5)

Total: 20

Exercise 6.15

Translate the following into Latin:

1 The mother of the king was beautiful. (4)

2 You (pl.) had many spears. (3)

3 I will give a present to the young man. (3)

4 The boys were running from the fields to the town. (6)

5 We were making a journey away from the city. (4)

Total: 20

Exercise 6.16

Give and translate the following:

1 The 1st person singular, future tense of adeo.

2 The 3rd person singular, imperfect tense of sum.

3 The 3rd person plural, perfect tense of eo.

4 The 2nd person plural, perfect tense of rideo.

5 The 2nd person singular, imperfect tense of pugno.

2 marks for each question. Total: 10

Exercise 6.17

Give the translation, person, number, tense and the 1st person singular of the present tense of the following verbs:

1 erit.

2 dedisti.

3 nuntiabunt.

4 advenerunt.

5 redibamus.

5 marks for each question. Total: 25

Exercise 6.18

Translate the following into English:

1 multi iuvenes ad urbem cras ibunt. (6)

2 mulier, quamquam pulchra erat, coniugem non habebat. (7)

3 in itinere lucem claram vidimus. (5)

4 mater in villa sola manebat. (5)

5 et pater et mater in bello perierunt. (7)

6 ubi ad urbem advenimus, ibi diu mansimus. (7)

7 Marcus laborabat. ceteri discipuli prope flumen ludebant. (7)

8 iuvenem vidi. ad urbem ibat. (5)

9 dominus multa dona servis cras dabit. (6)

10 uxor regis multos servos habebat. (5)

Total: 60

Exercise 6.19

Put into the plural and translate your answer:

1 femina ibat. (2 + 2)

2 trans flumen transeo. (2 + 3)

3 puella cras veniet. (2 + 3)

4 ad urbem ibam. (2 + 3)

5 iuvenis librum scripsit. (3 + 3)

Total: 25

Exercise 6.20

Put into the singular and translate your answer:

1 ad oppida adibatis. (2 + 3)

2 mulieres pulchrae erant. (3 + 3)

3 mox adveniemus. (1 + 2)

4 iuvenes perierunt. (2 + 2)

5 etiam servi templa viderunt. (3 + 4)

Total: 25

Exercise 7.1

Translate the following passage. Line numbers are given on the left. New words are underlined in the text and their meanings given in the margin.

Paris leaves Troy, goes to the Greek city of Sparta and kidnaps Menelaus' wife Helen

1 Helena mulier pulchra et clara erat. in urbe
Sparta cum viro, Menelao nomine, habitabat.
Paris vir clarus erat. in urbe Troia habitabat.
Troia erat urbs in Asia <u>sita</u>.

    sita = situated
    navis, -is, f. = ship
    descendit = disembarked, got off

5 Paris ex urbe Troia ad urbem Spartam
navigavit. ubi advenit, Paris e <u>nave</u> <u>descendit</u> et
ad <u>regiam</u> festinavit. ibi puellam Helenam vidit.
ubi Helenam vidit, <u>eam</u> statim amavit.

    regia, -ae, f. = palace
    eam = her

    Paris Helenae 'te amo,' inquit, 'Helena. veni! ex
10 urbe Sparta navigabimus et ad urbem Troiam
ibimus! festina!'

    Paris Helenam ad navem duxit. deinde
celeriter <u>fugerunt</u>. Paris et Helena ad urbem
Troiam navigaverunt. Paris laetus erat.
15 Menelaus <u>autem</u>, vir Helenae, non laetus sed
<u>iratissimus</u> erat.

    fugio, -ere, fugi (3½) = I flee

    autem = however
    iratissimus, -a, -um = very angry

Total: 100

Exercise 7.2

1 From the passage give, in Latin, one example of each of the following:

    (a) a conjunction.   (1)

    (b) an adverb.   (1)

2 urbe (line 1). In which case is this noun? Why is this case used?   (2)

3 nomine (line 2). In which case is this noun?   (1)

4 ibimus (line 11). Give the person, number and tense of this verb.
Give the 1st person singular of the present tense of this verb.   (4)

5 fugerunt (line 13). Explain the connection between this word and
the English word *fugitive*.   (1)

Total: 10

→ Verbs

Exercise 7.3

Translate the following into English:

1 fugiunt.

2 flebat.

3 oppugnabis.

4 cucurrerunt.

5 constituerunt.

6 discedemus.

7 advenisti.

8 aderat.

9 iecit.

10 misimus.

11 superabimus.

12 oppugnaverunt.

13 currebas.

14 superavit.

15 erras.

16 dormiemus.

17 fuerunt.

18 constituam.

19 discessit.

20 dabit.

1 mark for each question. Total: 20

Exercise 7.4

Translate the following into English:

1 iussit.

2 ponam.

3 fugiemus.

4 cupiebamus.

5 timebat.

6 nuntiavit.

7 rexit.

8 advenio.

9 duxit.

10 iubeo.

11 adveniam.

12 movemus.

13 mittunt.

14 tradidi.

15 posuerunt.

16 oppugnabatis.

17 dicebat.

18 iusserunt.

19 erraverunt.

20 damus.

1 mark for each question. Total: 20

Exercise 7.5

Translate the following into English:

1 stas.

2 dedimus.

3 fugiebamus.

4 movit.

5 movet.

6 fuit.

7 aberant.

8 scribemus.

9 fugerunt.

10 delebimus.

11 discesserunt.

12 appropinquabant.

13 regebat.

14 iaciebam.

15 scripsit.

16 tradidit.

17 deleverunt.

18 erunt.

19 fles.

20 stetit.

1 mark for each question. Total: 20

Exercise 7.6

Translate the following into Latin:

1 We shall arrive.

2 They ran.

3 He ordered.

4 They decided.

5 They were watching.

6 They fled.

7 They will sail.

8 He announced.

9 She called.

10 They were.

11 They went.

12 He was walking.

13 We are sailing.

14 He is arriving.

15 I shall run.

16 They fought.

17 You (pl.) will send.

18 We shall flee.

19 You (sing.) are standing.

20 We were laughing.

1 mark for each question. Total: 20

Exercise 7.7

Translate the following into Latin:

1 They were building.

2 We were playing.

3 She went.

4 You (sing.) will stay.

5 I kill.

6 They were approaching.

7 We were drinking.

8 He was holding.

9 We were throwing.

10 He asked.

11 I shall announce.

12 They replied.

13 I shall order.

14 They were going.

15 He captured.

16 I am reading.

17 We were.

18 We sent.

19 You (sing.) have built.

20 He punished.

1 mark for each question. Total: 20

Exercise 7.8

Translate the following into Latin:

1 I shall return.

2 I heard.

3 We shall see.

4 You (pl.) have given.

5 They told.

6 We saw.

7 He destroyed.

8 I shall be.

9 They stayed.

10 We departed.

11 It is departing.

12 You (pl.) were perishing.

13 I have written.

14 We are.

15 We shall decide.

16 He was running.

17 They threw.

18 She was fighting.

19 I shall destroy.

20 He saw.

1 mark for each question. Total: 20

Exercise 7.9

Translate the following into Latin:

1 The ship was approaching. (2)

2 We will attack the city tomorrow. (3)

3 Sailors like ships. (3)

4 Father did not have money. (4)

5 The rest of the pupils were working. (3)

Total: 15

Exercise 7.10

Translate the following into Latin:

1 Mother was on a ship.

2 We saw a ship near the island.

3 The slaves fled from the city.

4 The ships were returning to the island.

5 The ship was sailing on the river.

4 marks for each question. Total: 20

Chapter 7

Exercise 7.11

Put into the plural and translate your answer:

1 iam fugio.   (1 + 2)

2 navis pulchra appropinquabat.   (3 + 3)

3 equus dormiet.   (2 + 2)

4 rex terram rexit.   (3 + 3)

5 puella periculum timebat.   (3 + 3)

Total: 25

Exercise 7.12

Put into the singular and translate your answer:

1 diu currebatis.   (1 + 2)

2 matres miserae flebant.   (3 + 3)

3 servi fugerunt.   (2 + 2)

4 agricolae agros habent.   (3 + 3)

5 discipuli libros legebant.   (3 + 3)

Total: 25

Exercise 7.13

Keeping the same person and number, put the following verbs into the imperfect tense, then translate your answer:

1 narravit.   6 pugnavit.

2 erraverunt.   7 mansi.

3 ambulavimus.   8 cantavisti.

4 risistis.   9 vidit.

5 timuerunt.   10 clamavit.

2 marks for each question. Total: 20

Exercise 8.1

Translate the following passage. Line numbers are given on the left. New words are underlined in the text and their meanings given in the margin.

Menelaus appeals for help from other cities in Greece

1 Menelaus iratus erat. iratus erat quod Paris
uxorem, Helenam nomine, Troiam duxerat.
Menelaus hunc virum punire et hanc urbem
delere cupiebat.

5 nuntios igitur ad omnes urbes Graeciae misit.
hi nuntii haec verba dixerunt: 'audite, omnes!
Paris Helenam, uxorem caram Menelai, cepit.
Troiam fugit. propter hoc Menelaus iratus
est. hanc urbem delere cupit. arma parate!
10 naves et milites colligite! Troiam
navigabimus et Troianos puniemus!'

Graeci, ubi haec verba audiverunt, multas
copias paraverunt. copiae Graecorum ad
portum, Aulidem nomine, venerunt. Menelaus,
15 ubi has naves et hos milites vidit, laetus erat.
omnes salutavit. Troiam statim navigare et
bellum contra Troianos gerere et Helenam
liberare cupivit.

duxerat = had led
hunc/hanc = this
omnes = all
hi/haec = these
omnes = all, everyone
carus, -a, -um = dear
propter = on account of
hoc = this
arma, armorum, n.pl. =
arms, weapons
miles, militis, m. = soldier
colligo, -ere, collegi (3) =
I collect
Troianus, -a, -um = Trojan
copiae, copiarum, f.pl. =
forces, troops
portum = port
Aulidem = accusative case
of Aulis (a name, Greek form)
has/hos = these
saluto, -are, -avi (1) = I greet
gero, -ere, gessi (3) = I wage
libero, -are, -avi (1) = I set
free

Total: 105

Exercise 8.2

1 From the passage give, in Latin, one example of each of the following:

   (a) an infinitive. (1)

   (b) a preposition. (1)

   (c) an imperative. (1)

   (d) a verb in the future tense. (1)

2 nuntios (line 5). In which case is this noun? Why is this case used? (2)

3 misit (line 5). Give the person, number and tense of this verb. Give the 1st person singular of the present tense of this verb. (4)

Total: 10

➜ hic, haec, hoc = this

Exercise 8.3

Translate the following into English:

1 hic miles.
2 hic rex.
3 hoc scutum.
4 haec urbs.
5 hae urbes.
6 hic servus.
7 haec mater.
8 hi pueri.
9 hae naves.
10 hoc donum.

11 haec corpora.
12 hi reges.
13 hi milites.
14 hoc iter.
15 hic puer.
16 hi servi.
17 hi agricolae.
18 hoc flumen.
19 haec verba.
20 haec uxor.

2 marks for each question. Total: 40

Exercise 8.4

Translate the following into English:

1 huius puellae.
2 huius militis.
3 horum militum.
4 harum navium.
5 hoc dono.
6 hoc bello.
7 hac luce.
8 huius pueri.
9 horum servorum.
10 his verbis.

11 hoc gladio.
12 huic servo.
13 harum mulierum.
14 hoc vulnere.
15 hoc nomine.
16 his vulneribus.
17 his nominibus.
18 huic iuveni.
19 his fluminibus.
20 huius regis.

2 marks for each question. Total: 40

Exercise 8.5

Translate the following into English:

1 hic puer est Marcus.   (4)
2 hoc bellum est malum.   (4)
3 hi pueri sunt parvi.   (4)
4 hae puellae sunt parvae.   (4)
5 hanc puellam amo.   (3)

6 haec verba audio. (3)

7 rex hunc militem punit. (4)

8 puella hunc cibum non amat. (5)

9 dominus pecuniam his servis dabit. (5)

10 haec flumina longa sunt. (4)

Total: 40

Exercise 8.6

Translate the following into English:

1 templum huius dei magnum est. (5)

2 libri horum puerorum boni sunt. (5)

3 multam pecuniam huic puero do. (5)

4 pecuniam his pueris non do. (5)

5 magister puerum hoc gladio necat. (5)

6 magister pueros his verbis terret. (5)

7 librum huius pueri lego. (4)

8 iuvenis, ubi haec verba audivit, discessit. (6)

9 Romani Graecos his militibus mox superabunt. (6)

10 hoc flumen sacrum est. (4)

Total: 50

Exercise 8.7

Translate the following into Latin:

1 This soldier.

2 These soldiers.

3 This city.

4 These cities.

5 This river.

6 These rivers.

7 These weapons.

8 These forces.

9 This light.

10 This journey.

2 marks for each question. Total: 20

Exercise 8.8

Translate the following into Latin:

1 These young men.

2 This mother.

3 These presents.

4 This shield.

5 These dangers.

6 This pupil.

7 These fields.

8 This teacher.

9 These walls.

10 This crowd.

2 marks for each question. Total: 20

Exercise 8.9

Translate the following into Latin:

1 For this girl.

2 Of these farmers.

3 To this queen

4 By this road.

5 Of these Romans.

6 With these arrows.

7 With this food.

8 For this horse.

9 Of these walls.

10 Of this book.

2 marks for each question. Total: 20

Exercise 8.10

Translate the following into Latin:

1 This ship was sailing to the island.

2 I saw this beautiful girl yesterday.

3 The messenger returned to this city.

4 I was carrying this body out of the town.

5 The soldiers have collected all these weapons.

5 marks for each question. Total: 25

Exercise 8.11

Translate the following into Latin:

1 The name of this girl is Flavia.

2 The walls of this city are tall.

3 The soldier has fought well with this sword.

4 The master will give a present to these slaves.

5 The girls liked the villa of this young man.

5 marks for each question. Total: 25

Exercise 8.12

Translate the following into Latin:

1 The forces were approaching. (2)

2 The master set free the slave. (3)

3 We greeted father. (2)

4 The soldier was fighting well. (3)

5 The young man will collect the weapons. (3)

6 The soldiers collected many weapons. (4)

7 The Romans had great forces. (4)

8 The king killed the soldier in battle. (5)

9 Many soldiers perished because of the war. (5)

10 The arms of the soldiers were new. (4)

Total: 35

Exercise 8.13

Put into the plural and translate your answer:

1 liberas. (1 + 1)

2 miles bonus est. (3 + 3)

3 navis cras adveniet. (2 + 3)

4 dominus servum liberabit. (3 + 3)

5 puer patrem salutavit. (3 + 3)

Total: 25

Exercise 8.14

Put into the singular and translate your answer:

1 scuta hastasque collegerunt. (3 + 3)

2 iuvenes fugiebant. (2 + 2)

3 milites pugnabant. (2 + 2)

4 mulieres cras redibunt. (2 + 3)

5 puellae equos amabunt. (3 + 3)

Total: 25

Exercise 8.15

Give and translate the following:

1 The 3rd person singular, perfect tense of libero.

2 The 1st person singular, imperfect tense of saluto.

3 The 2nd person plural, perfect tense of gero.

4 The 3rd person plural, perfect tense of fugio.

5 The 1st person plural, future tense of eo.

2 marks for each question. Total: 10

Exercise 8.16

Give the translation, person, number, tense and 1st person singular of the present tense of the following verbs:

1 exierunt.

2 erat.

3 gessit.

4 bibemus.

5 colligam.

5 marks for each question. Total: 25

Exercise 9.1

Translate the following passage. Line numbers are given on the left. New words are underlined in the text and their meanings given in the margin.

The Greeks assemble at Aulis, but their departure is delayed by contrary winds

1 Graeci multos milites et multas naves
   <u>Aulidem</u> miserunt. Menelaus, ubi <u>illos</u> milites
   et <u>illas</u> naves <u>conspexit</u>, laetus erat. Troiam
   non amabat. <u>illam</u> urbem <u>sine</u> <u>mora</u> delere
5 cupiebat.

   naves tamen navigare non <u>poterant</u>. naves
   navigare non <u>poterant</u> quod venti <u>adversi</u>
   erant. Graeci prope naves diu manserunt. nihil
   faciebant. diu ventos <u>secundos</u>
10 <u>exspectaverunt</u>. <u>nemo</u> laetus erat. sed tandem
   venti <u>secundi</u> erant.

   Menelaus militibus clamavit: '<u>comites</u>, <u>illi</u> venti
   nunc <u>secundi</u> sunt. parate naves! parate arma!
   discedere <u>debemus</u>!

15 Graeci, ubi haec verba audiverunt, naves
   celeriter paraverunt et <u>Aulide</u> navigaverunt.

Aulidem = to Aulis
illos = those
illas = those
conspicio, -ere, conspexi
(3½) = I catch sight of
illam = that
sine + abl. = without
mora, -ae, f. = delay
poterant = (they) were able
adversus, -a, -um =
contrary
secundus, -a, -um =
favourable
exspecto, -are, -avi (1) =
I wait for
nemo = no one
comes, comitis, m./f. =
companion
illi = those
debeo, -ere, debui +
infinitive (2) = I must, have to
Aulide = from Aulis

Total: 85

Exercise 9.2

1 From the passage give, in Latin, one example of each of the following:

   (a) a conjunction.   (1)

   (b) a preposition.   (1)

   (c) a verb in the perfect tense.   (1)

   (d) a verb in the imperfect tense.   (1)

2 manserunt (line 8). Give the person and number of this verb. Give the 1st
   person singular of the present tense of this verb.   (3)

3 naves (line 13). Give the case of this noun. Why is this case used?   (2)

4 verba (line 15). Give the gender of this noun.   (1)

Total: 10

Exercise 9.3

Translate the following into English:

1 ille servus.

2 illa navis.

3 illud bellum.

4 illi hostes.

5 illae urbes.

6 illa bella.

7 illa mulier.

8 illa arma.

9 illa corpora.

10 illud flumen.

11 illi equi.

12 ille comes.

13 illa puella.

14 illae copiae.

15 illa verba.

16 illud oppidum.

17 ille iuvenis.

18 illi comites.

19 ille amicus.

20 illi milites.

2 marks for each question. Total: 40

Exercise 9.4

Translate the following into English:

1 illius equi.

2 illis amicis.

3 illorum puerorum.

4 illi mulieri.

5 in illa urbe.

6 illarum puellarum.

7 illi deo.

8 illorum iuvenum.

9 illo itinere.

10 illis armis.

11 illis militibus.

12 illi servo.

13 illorum periculorum.

14 illa luce.

15 illis sagittis.

16 illorum magistrorum.

17 illius amici.

18 illarum feminarum.

19 illius urbis.

20 illi servo.

2 marks for each question. Total: 40

Exercise 9.5

Translate the following into English:

1 ille servus bonus est. (4)

2 illa puella pulchra est. (4)

3 illi milites fessi sunt. (4)

4 illa navis magna est. (4)

5 illud templum magnum et pulchrum est. (6)

6 illa verba mala sunt. (4)

7 illum puerum non amo. (4)

8 dominus illos servos saepe punit. (5)

9 magister illas puellas non amat. (5)

10 nomen illius pueri est Marcus. (5)

Total: 45

Exercise 9.6

Translate the following into English:

1 scuta illorum militum magna sunt. (5)

2 pecuniam illis servis cras dabo. (5)

3 dux arma illi militi dat. (5)

4 puer puellam pulchram illo gladio necabit. (6)

5 mater mea illa dona amabit. (5)

6 illa verba amo. (3)

7 multi iuvenes in illa urbe habitant. (6)

8 sunt multae naves in illo flumine. (6)

9 ubi sunt libri illorum puerorum? (5)

10 illud flumen sacrum est. (4)

Total: 50

Exercise 9.7

Translate the following into English:

1 hic servus bonus, ille malus est. (6)

2 haec insula magna, illa parva est. (6)

3 ille servus hunc dominum timebat. (5)

4 hic dominus illum servum terrebat. (5)

5 illi milites hanc urbem oppugnaverunt. (5)

6 illi iuvenes has puellas spectabant. (5)

7 haec navis ad illam insulam navigavit. (6)

8 illi servi ex hoc oppido fugerunt. (6)

9 hanc puellam in illa via vidi. (6)

10 ille dominus hos servos puniebat. (5)

Total: 55

Exercise 9.8

Translate the following into Latin:

1 That sword.

2 That woman.

3 That war.

4 Those horses.

5 Those girls.

6 Those temples.

7 That delay.

8 Those companions.

9 That soldier.

10 Those soldiers.

2 marks for each question. Total: 20

Exercise 9.9

Translate the following into Latin:

1 Those ships.

2 That light.

3 That name.

4 That city.

5 Those young men.

6 That journey.

7 Those rivers.

8 That danger.

9 That pupil.

10 Those books.

2 marks for each question. Total: 20

Exercise 9.10

Translate the following into Latin:

1 Of that boy.

2 Of that girl.

3 Of that war.

4 Of those boys.

5 Of those girls.

6 Of those wars.

7 For that slave.

8 To those slaves.

9 By those words.

10 By that present.

2 marks for each question. Total: 20

Exercise 9.11

Translate the following into Latin:

1 To those companions.

2 For that soldier.

3 Of that ship.

4 By that light.

5 Of those bodies.

6 To those young men.

7 To that king.

8 To that city.

9 By that name.

10 For those friends.

2 marks for each question. Total: 20

Exercise 9.12

Translate the following into Latin:

1 I like that girl.

2 I am watching those ships.

3 I am crossing that river.

4 I am setting free those slaves.

5 I am attacking that city.

3 marks for each question. Total: 15

Exercise 9.13

Translate the following into Latin:

1 The teacher does not like those pupils.   (5)

2 That ship will arrive soon.   (4)

3 The master never gives money to those slaves.   (6)

4 The master of those slaves is wicked.   (5)

5 The soldier wounded the friend with that sword.   (5)

Total: 25

Exercise 9.14

Translate the following into Latin:

1 We attacked the city without delay.   (4)

2 The companions have returned today.   (3)

3 No one caught sight of the ship.   (3)

4 Those soldiers were fighting.   (3)

5 We are waiting for the queen.   (2)

Total: 15

Exercise 9.15

Translate the following into Latin:

1 My companions will arrive soon.   (4)

2 The king caught sight of the famous soldier in the crowd. (6)

3 The girl waited for the friend in the town for a long time. (6)

4 I saw this boy in the city.   (5)

5 My companion perished in the war.   (4)

Total: 25

Exercise 9.16

Put into the plural and translate your answer:

1 bellum diu gessit.   (2 + 3)

2 mater exspectabat.   (2 + 2)

3 comes currebat.   (2 + 2)

4 puella pulchra erat.   (3 + 3)

5 nauta navem conspexit.   (3 + 3)

Total: 25

Exercise 9.17

Put into the singular and translate your answer:

1 frustra fugiebamus.   (1 + 2)

2 milites discesserunt.   (2 + 2)

3 illae naves magnae erant.   (4 + 4)

4 dona mittemus.   (2 + 2)

5 Graeci hastas collegerunt.   (3 + 3)

Total: 25

Exercise 10.1

Translate the following passage. Line numbers are given on the left. New words are underlined in the text and their meanings given in the margin.

Protesilaus: hero or half wit?

1 quod venti <u>secundi</u> erant, Graeci naves
    paraverunt. deinde in <u>eis</u> trans mare celeriter
    navigaverunt. ubi autem naves ad terram
    appropinquaverunt, nemo e Graecis e navibus
5 <u>descendere</u> cupiebat, <u>nam</u> dei haec verba
    Graecis <u>dixerant</u>: '<u>is qui</u> primus in terram
    <u>Troianam</u> <u>descendet, primus occidetur</u>.'

    diu Graeci nihil fecerunt. <u>inter</u> <u>eos</u> autem erat
    miles, Protesilaus nomine. hic miles <u>mortem</u> non
10 timebat. clamavit: 'spectate me, comites! ego
    <u>fortis</u> sum. ego <u>audax</u> sum. ego primus in terram
    Troianam <u>descendam</u>. <u>sic</u> ego clarus ero.'

    Protesilaus in terram statim <u>descendit</u>. ubi <u>is</u>
    descendit, ceteri Graeci <u>descenderunt</u>.
15 postquam Protesilaus <u>Troianos</u> vidit, contra
    eos <u>ruit</u>. multos ex <u>eis</u> <u>occidit</u>. tandem tamen,
    postquam multa <u>vulnera</u> <u>accepit</u>, periit. <u>sic</u>
    clarus <u>factus est</u>.

secundus, -a, -um = favourable
eis = them
descendo, -ere, descendi (3) = I climb down, disembark
nam = for
dixerant = had said
is = he
qui = who
Troianus, -a, -um = Trojan
primus occidetur = will be the first killed
inter + acc. = among
eos = them
mors, mortis, f. = death
fortis = brave
audax = daring
sic = in this way, thus
ruo, -ere, rui (3) = I charge
occido, -ere, occidi (3) = I kill
vulnus, vulneris, n. = wound
accipio, -ere, accepi (3½) = I receive
factus est = he became

Total: 105

Exercise 10.2

1 From the passage give, in Latin, one example of each of the following:

   (a) a demonstrative adjective. (1)

   (b) a 3rd declension noun. (1)

   (c) an ordinal number. (1)

2 **venti** (line 1). Explain the connection between this word and the English word *ventilation*. (1)

3 **navibus** (line 4). In which case is this noun? Why is this case used? (2)

4 **fecerunt** (line 8). In which tense is this verb? Give the 1st person singular of the present tense of this verb. (2)

5 **vidit** (line 15). Give the Latin subject and Latin object of this verb. (2)

Total: 10

→ is, ea, id = that / he, she, it

The pronoun **is, ea, id** means 'that' (pl. 'those') but is also used to mean 'he', 'she' or 'it'. As a general rule, if **is, ea, id** is used in agreement with a noun, it means 'that', or 'those'. If not, it means 'he', 'she' or 'it'.

Exercise 10.3

Translate the following into English:

1 Menelaus miles Graecus erat. is vir bonus erat.   (8)

2 Helena uxor Menelai erat. ea femina pulchra erat.   (8)

3 in urbe est templum. id est templum magnum.   (8)

4 Marcus filium habet. eum amat.   (5)

5 Marcus filiam habet. eam amat.   (5)

6 Marcus filium et filiam habet. eos amat.   (7)

7 Marcus servum habet. pecuniam ei dat.   (6)

8 insula magna est. multi incolae in ea habitant.   (8)

9 Marcus multos libros accipit. eos semper legit.   (7)

10 Marcus uxorem pulchram habet. nomen eius est Aurelia.   (8)

Total: 70

Exercise 10.4

Translate the following into English:

1 Aurelia multos amicos habet. amici eius clari sunt.   (8)

2 Marcus et Aurelia multos servos habent. servi eorum boni sunt.   (10)

3 Marcus pecuniam eis saepe dat.   (5)

4 Marcus librum legit. sunt in eo multa verba.   (8)

5 Marcus vinum ad Aureliam misit. ea id nunc bibit.   (9)

6 Marcus multa arma habet. arma eius nova sunt.   (8)

7 Marcus multa arma habet. ea amat.   (6)

8 rex servos amat. multam pecuniam eis saepe dat.   (8)

9 servus aquam rogat. dominus eam ei dat.   (7)

10 templum novum est. id nunc spectamus.   (6)

Total: 75

Exercise 10.5

Translate the following into English:

1 magister hunc servum non amabat. eum igitur puniebat. (8)

2 Protesilaus fortiter pugnabat. Troiani tamen eum mox occiderunt. (8)

3 Graeci contra Troianos ruerunt. multos ex eis necaverunt. (8)

4 ille miles multa vulnera accepit. vulnera eius mala erant. (9)

5 dominus servum bonum, Sextum nomine, habebat. eum heri liberavit. (9)

6 navis magna erat. erant in ea multi nautae. (8)

7 magister multa verba dixit. nemo tamen ea audiebat. (8)

8 multae puellae appropinquabant. eas mox conspeximus. (6)

9 Romani milites boni erant. Graeci eos non superaverunt. (8)

10 agricolae multos agros habebant. agri eorum magni erant. (8)

Total: 80

Exercise 10.6

Translate the following into English:

1 ubi amicus venit, vir eum salutavit. (6)

2 magister meus uxorem pulchram habet. eam saepe video. (8)

3 illa femina pulchra erat. multi viri eam amabant. (8)

4 urbs magna erat. Romani eam capere constituerunt. (7)

5 hoc vinum bonum est. id saepe bibo. (7)

6 Graeci multa arma collegerunt. ea in navibus posuerunt. (8)

7 Menelaus et Helena Graeci erant. is clarus, ea pulchra erat. (10)

8 quod servi boni erant, dominus multam pecuniam eis dedit. (9)

9 puer, quod puellam amabat, multa dona ei dabat. (8)

10 auxilio eorum urbem cepimus. (4)

Total: 75

Exercise 10.7

Translate the following into Latin:

1 I have a brother. I like him. (4)

2 I have a sister. I like her. (4)

3 I have a name. I do not like it. (5)

4 I have horses. I love them. (4)

5 I have daughters. I love them. (4)

57

6 I have many presents. I like them. (5)

7 I do not like his brother. (4)

8 I like the girls; I do not like their mother. (6)

9 Their weapons are new. (4)

10 I have slaves. I give money to them. (5)

Total: 45

Exercise 10.8

Put into the plural and translate your answer:

1 scripsi. (1 + 1)

2 miles periit. (2 + 2)

3 vulnus accepit. (2 + 2)

4 mulier dormiebat. (2 + 2)

5 puer amicum habet. (3 + 3)

Total: 20

Exercise 10.9

Put into the plural and translate your answer:

1 comes currit.

2 puellam conspexi.

3 navem exspectabat.

4 vulnus accepi.

5 servus ruebat.

2 + 2 marks for each question. Total: 20

Exercise 10.10

Put into the singular and translate your answer:

1 amici fuerunt. (2 + 2)

2 reges currebant. (2 + 2)

3 milites occidimus. (2 + 2)

4 ancillae scuta non portabant. (3 + 4)

5 reges comites occiderunt. (3 + 3)

Total: 25

Exercise 10.11

Put into the singular and translate your answer:

1 Romani erant. (2 + 2)

2 vulnera mala sunt. (3 + 3)

3 comites pugnabant. (2 + 2)

4 servi fugerunt. (2 + 2)

5 ivistis. (1 + 1)

Total: 20

Exercise 10.12

Give and translate the following:

1 The 3rd person plural, imperfect tense of **exspecto**.

2 The 3rd person singular, perfect tense of **conspicio**.

3 The 1st person singular, future tense of **ruo**.

4 The 2nd person plural, imperfect tense of **occido**.

5 The 2nd person singular, present tense of **eo**.

2 marks for each question. Total: 10

Exercise 10.13

Give the translation, person, number, tense and 1st person singular of the present tense of the following:

1 conspexerunt. 4 occidit.

2 exspectabas. 5 accepimus.

3 ruet.

5 marks for each question. Total: 25

Exercise 10.14

Translate the following into Latin:

1 I do not fear death.

2 The boy received a gift.

3 The Greeks will kill the Romans.

4 We received many wounds.

5 My companions have come.

3 marks for each question. Total: 15

Exercise 10.15

Translate the following into Latin:

1 We will charge against the Romans tomorrow. (4)

2 We will attack the city with weapons. (3)

3 Death will come to the old man soon. (4)

4 The wounds of the king are bad. (3)

5 The ship did not arrive today because of the delay. (6)

Total: 20

Exercise 11.1

Translate the following passage. Line numbers are given on the left. New words are underlined in the text and their meanings given in the margin.

The Greeks realise that capturing Troy will not be a five-minute job

1 Protesilaus <u>mortuus</u> erat. Graeci contra
   muros Troiae ruerunt. fortiter et diu <u>sub</u>
   muris pugnaverunt, sed <u>frustra</u>. urbem non
   ceperunt. non multos Troianos <u>vulneraverunt</u>.
5 non multos Troianos occiderunt.

   Agamemnon, frater Menelai, <u>dux</u> Graecorum
   erat. non laetus erat. haec verba militibus dixit:
   'Graeci, haec verba <u>vobis</u> dico: Troiam hodie
   non capiemus. muri Troiae alti et validi sunt.
10 illi <u>cives</u> Troiani <u>fortes</u> sunt. muros bene
   <u>defendunt</u>. ego vos <u>castra</u> ponere iubeo. bene
   dormite! cras contra <u>hostes</u> iterum
   pugnare debebimus.'

   milites Graeci verbis Agamemnonis
15 <u>paruerunt</u>. castra posuerunt. fessi erant. mox
   dormiebant.

mortuus, -a, -um = dead
sub + abl. = under
frustra = in vain
vulnero, -are, -avi (1) = I wound

dux, ducis, m. = leader, general

vobis = to you
civis, civis, m. = citizen

fortis, -is, -e = brave
defendo, -ere, defendi (3) = I defend
castra, -orum, n.pl. = camp
hostes, -ium, m.pl. = enemy
pareo, -ere, parui (2) + dat. = I obey

Total: 85

Exercise 11.2

1 From the passage give, in Latin, one example of each of the following:

  (a) an adverb. (1)

  (b) a noun in the genitive case. (1)

  (c) an infinitive. (1)

2 mortuus (line 1). Explain the connection between this word and the English word *mortuary*. (1)

3 muros (line 2). In which case is this noun? Why is this case used? (2)

4 ceperunt (line 4). Give the 1st person singular of the present tense of this verb. (1)

5 debebimus (line 13). Give the person, number and tense of this verb. (3)

Total: 10

→ ego and tu

Exercise 11.3

Translate the following into English:

1 tu ludis; ego laboro. (4)

2 nos Romani sumus; vos Graeci estis. (6)

3 nos vos non amamus. (4)

4 vos nos non amatis. (4)

5 ego te non amo. (4)

6 tu me non amas. (4)

7 nemo me vidit. (3)

8 ego puellam amo. (3)

9 puella me non amat. (4)

10 te in urbe vidi. (4)

Total: 40

Exercise 11.4

Translate the following into English:

1 hostes nos oppugnant. (3)

2 Romani nos non amant. (4)

3 pater meus te amat. (4)

4 te puniam, serve! (3)

5 quis me vocat? (3)

6 magister te vocat. (3)

7 femina nos spectat. (3)

8 quis pecuniam mihi dabit? (4)

9 ego multam pecuniam tibi dabo. (5)

10 puellae nobiscum ludent. (3)

Total: 35

Exercise 11.5

Translate the following into English:

1 servus prope me stat. (4)

2 hostes contra nos pugnant. (4)

3 pater pecuniam tibi dat. (4)

4 dominus pecuniam vobis dabit, servi. (5)

Chapter 11

5 servi ad me festinant. (4)

6 amici mecum ludunt. (3)

7 ego donum tibi dabo. (4)

8 magister dona nobis numquam dat. (5)

9 pater donum mihi, tibi pecuniam dedit. (6)

10 ille magister te, non me, amat. (6)

Total: 45

Exercise 11.6

Translate the following into Latin:

1 I am Roman; you are Greek. (6)

2 We are good; you are bad. (6)

3 I am giving money to you. (4)

4 He often gives money to us. (4)

5 Play with me, friends! (3)

6 We do not wish to play with you. (3)

7 That girl will never give me a present. (6)

8 The teacher will punish you, but not me. (6)

9 He is doing this for us. (4)

10 Come with us, mother! (3)

Total: 45

Exercise 11.7

Put into the plural and translate your answer:

1 te cras videbo. (2 + 3)

2 hasta servum vulneravit. (3 + 3)

3 rex mortuus erat. (3 + 3)

4 miles navem exspectabat. (3 + 3)

5 dux bellum non timet. (3 + 4)

Total: 30

Exercise 11.8

Put into the singular and translate your answer:

1 pueri mortui non currunt. (3 + 4)

2 cur nos monebitis? (2 + 3)

3   milites reges vulnerabant.   (3 + 3)

4   cives oppida defenderunt.   (3 + 3)

5   duces comites amabant.   (3 + 3)

Total: 30

Exercise 11.9

Translate the following into English:

1   illi milites in proelio fortiter pugnaverunt.   (6)

2   hunc civem in urbe heri conspexi.   (6)

3   multae naves insulam contra hostes defendebant.   (6)

4   quod milites bene pugnabant, dux eos laudavit.   (7)

5   Romani bella contra Graecos saepe gerebant.   (6)

6   arma militum Romanorum nova erant.   (5)

7   comites ab insula in navibus sine mora discesserunt.   (8)

8   hostes multos cives armis vulneraverunt.   (5)

9   ille magister, quod ego numquam laborabam, me non amabat.   (9)

10 copiae hostium multa vulnera a nobis acceperunt.   (7)

Total: 65

Exercise 11.10

Translate the following into Latin:

1   The Roman citizen was dead.   (4)

2   We were fighting against the enemy.   (3)

3   The good citizens defended the city well.   (5)

4   The spears wounded the soldiers.   (3)

5   The enemy were fighting well for a long time.   (4)

6   The citizens hurried to the city.   (4)

7   The enemy wounded the king with arrows.   (4)

8   Good leaders do not fear death.   (5)

9   We saw the enemy in the city.   (4)

10 The wounds of the citizen were bad.   (4)

Total: 40

12

Exercise 12.1

Translate the following passage. Line numbers are given on the left. New words are underlined in the text and their meanings given in the margin.

Achilles and Hector

1 Graeci Troiam <u>oppugnaverant</u>. urbem Troiam tamen non statim <u>occupaverant</u>. Troianos non <u>vicerant</u>. prope urbem Troiam igitur <u>castra</u> <u>posuerant</u>.

5 diu copiae Graecorum muros Troiae oppugnabant. eos tamen delere non <u>poterant</u>. <u>omnes</u> Graeci igitur <u>iratissimi</u>, Troiani <u>laetissimi</u> erant.

   <u>Priamus</u> rex Troiae erat. multos <u>liberos</u> <u>fortes</u>
10 habebat. <u>nemo</u> autem <u>fortior</u> <u>aut</u> <u>clarior</u> <u>quam</u> Hector erat. vir magnae <u>virtutis</u> erat. <u>pro</u> Troianis fortiter pugnabat.

   inter Graecos quoque erant multi milites <u>fortes</u>. Achilles autem <u>fortissimus</u> erat.
15 Achilles amicum, <u>Patroclum</u> nomine, habebat. quod Hector <u>Patroclum</u> in proelio <u>occiderat</u>, Achilles <u>iratissimus</u> erat.

oppugnaverant = had attacked
occupaverant = they had seized
vicerant = they had conquered
castra, -orum, n.pl. = camp
posuerant = they had pitched

poterant = they were able
omnes = all
iratissimus, -a, -um = very angry
laetissimus, -a, -um = very happy
Priamus = Priam (a name)
liberi, -orum, m.pl. = children
fortis, -is, -e = brave
nemo = no one
fortior = braver
aut = or
clarior = more famous
quam = than
virtus, virtutis, f. = courage
pro + abl. = for
fortissimus, -a, -um = the bravest
Patroclum = Patroclus (a name)
occiderat = had killed

Total: 85

Exercise 12.2

1 From the passage give, in Latin, one example of each of the following:

   (a) an adverb.   (1)

   (b) a preposition.   (1)

   (c) an infinitive.   (1)

2 oppugnaverant (line 1). Give the Latin subject and the Latin object of this verb.   (2)

3 erant (line 8). Give the 1st person singular of the present tense of this verb. (1)

4 Troiae (line 9). In which case is this noun?   (1)

5 habebat (line 10). Give the person, number and tense of this verb.   (3)

Total: 10

➜ The pluperfect tense

Exercise 12.3

Translate the following into Latin:

1 He had loved.
2 They had carried.
3 We had stayed.
4 I had seen.
5 You (sing.) had sent.
6 They had put.
7 We had made.
8 You (pl.) had taken.
9 They had heard.
10 I had come.

11 She had slept.
12 He had punished.
13 You (sing.) had played.
14 He had given.
15 They had laughed.
16 We had fought.
17 They had departed.
18 I had read.
19 We had destroyed.
20 He had walked.

1 mark for each question. Total: 20

Exercise 12.4

Translate the following into Latin:

1 They had made.
2 He had seen.
3 You (sing.) had destroyed.
4 We had put.
5 I had laughed.

6 You (pl.) had punished.
7 He had made.
8 She had sent.
9 We had come.
10 They had taken.

1 mark for each question. Total: 10

Exercise 12.5

Translate the following into English:

1 amaveramus.
2 ceperant.
3 audiveras.
4 rexerat.
5 dederam.

6 duxerat.
7 moveramus.
8 terruerat.
9 responderant.
10 miseram.

1 mark for each question. Total: 10

Exercise 12.6

Translate the following into English:

1 posuerat.

2 cucurrerant.

3 discesseras.

4 legeram.

5 dormiveramus.

6 ambulaveramus.

7 fugerat.

8 feceratis.

9 riseramus.

10 deleveras.

1 mark for each question. Total: 10

Exercise 12.7

Translate the following into English:

1 manseramus.

2 viderant.

3 pugnaverat.

4 intraverant.

5 ceperat.

6 monueras.

7 biberat.

8 dixerat.

9 luseramus.

10 occideratis.

1 mark for each question. Total: 10

Exercise 12.8

Translate the following into English:

1 magister iratus erat quod riseramus. (5)

2 puer librum non legerat. (4)

3 pueri mali fuerant. (3)

4 puella puerum vulneraverat. (3)

5 verba non audiveramus. (3)

6 dominus laetus erat quod bene dormiverat. (6)

7 servi bene laboraverant. (3)

8 uxor discesserat. (5)

9 servus cibum paraverat. (3)

10 amicus multam pecuniam ei dederat. (5)

Total: 40

Exercise 12.9

Translate the following into English:

1 hostes laeti erant quod Romani discesserant. (6)

2 dei Romanos vicerant. (3)

3 numquam urbem deleverant. (3)

4 celeriter adveneramus. (2)

5 multa oppida ceperant. (3)

6 puer celeriter currebat quod magistrum iratum viderat. (7)

7 magister iratus eum conspexerat. (4)

8 miles validus eum terruerat. (4)

9 tandem is ducem occiderat. (4)

10 servus malus sororem vulneraverat. (4)

Total: 40

Exercise 12.10

Translate the following into English

1 puer diu laboraverat. (3)

2 dux iratus fuerat. (3)

3 milites bene pugnaverant. (3)

4 bene dormiveram. (2)

5 puer miser non riserat. (4)

6 proelium longum fuerat. (3)

7 hostes multas terras superaverant. (4)

8 dominus multos servos liberaverat. (4)

9 rex hostium ad flumen festinaverat. (5)

10 milites oppidum fortiter oppugnaverant. (4)

Total: 35

Exercise 12.11

Translate the following into English:

1 servi ex oppido cucurrerant. (4)

2 magister multos libros legerat. (4)

3 nuntius multa verba dixerat. (4)

4 servus multam aquam biberat. (4)

5 femina multa vulnera acceperat. (4)

6 puer donum ad patrem miserat. (5)

7 milites flumen transierant. (4)

8 puellam non conspexeramus. (3)

9 milites non bene pugnaverant. (4)

10 cives oppidum fortiter defenderant. (4)

Total: 40

Exercise 12.12

Translate the following into Latin:

1 We had conquered the enemy.

2 They had seized the city.

3 He had wounded the king.

4 We had defended the town.

5 I had seen the girl.

2 marks for each question. Total: 10

Exercise 12.13

Translate the following into Latin:

1 The leader had said many words.

2 The soldier had wounded the friend with a spear.

3 The enemy had charged against the town.

4 The sailors had waited for the ship for a long time.

5 The Greeks had collected many weapons.

4 marks for each question. Total: 20

Exercise 12.14

Give and translate the following:

1 The 3rd person plural, present tense of **occupo**.

2 The 1st person plural, imperfect tense of **defendo**.

3 The 2nd person plural, future tense of **vinco**.

4 The 2nd person singular, perfect tense of **vulnero**.

5 The 3rd person singular, perfect tense of **vinco**.

2 marks for each question. Total: 10

Exercise 12.15

Give the translation, person, number, tense and 1st person singular of the present tense of the following:

1 defendemus.

2 ibat.

3 vicerat.

4 eritis.

5 vulneravit.

5 marks for each question. Total: 25

Exercise 12.16

Put into the plural and translate your answer:

1 dux clarus erat.   (3 + 3)

2 urbem defendis.   (2 + 2)

3 dominus servum vulneraverat.   (3 + 3)

4 regem numquam conspexi.   (2 + 3)

5 oppidum occupabo.   (2 + 2)

Total: 25

Exercise 12.17

Put into the singular and translate your answer:

1 vincemus.   (1 + 1)

2 hastae vulnerant.   (2 + 2)

3 duces pugnaverant.   (2 + 2)

4 Romanos vicimus.   (2 + 2)

5 cives mortui erant.   (3 + 3)

Total: 20

Exercise 12.18

Translate the following into Latin:

1 I do not have the courage.

2 The enemy were savage.

3 We will never beat the enemy.

4 They will seize the town tomorrow.

5 The Romans have conquered the Greeks.

3 marks for each question. Total: 15

Exercise 12.19

Translate the following into Latin:

1　That man has great courage. (5)

2　The courage of those soldiers was famous. (4)

3　These citizens were defending the town well. (5)

4　The soldiers were attacking the city with great courage. (5)

5　I saw my companion in the city yesterday. (6)

Total: 25

Exercise 12.20

Keeping the same person and number, put the following verbs into the imperfect tense and translate your answer:

1 occupaverunt.

2 vulneravit.

3 exspectavimus.

4 mansimus.

5 liberavistis.

6 risit.

7 salutaverunt.

8 respondit.

9 rogavit.

10 dedi.

2 marks for each question. Total: 20

Exercise 13.1

Translate the following passage. Line numbers are given on the left. New words are underlined in the text and their meanings given in the margin.

Achilles, angry because of Patroclus' death, tells Hector that he will kill him. Hector is not impressed

1 Achilles iratus erat quod Hector Patroclum
   occiderat. Hectorem igitur occidere cupiebat.
   olim Troiani contra Graecos prope urbem
   Troiam pugnabant. omnes fortiter pugnabant.
5 tum subito Achilles Hectorem forte
   conspexit. ubi eum vidit, ei clamavit: 'audi me,
   Hector! ego sum Achilles, fortissimus
   Graecorum. tu vir crudelis es. quod tu
   Patroclum, amicum meum, occidisti, ego te
10 occidam!'

   Hector, ubi verba Achillis audivit, ei respondit:
   'audi verba mea, Achilles! laetus sum quod
   ego Patroclum, amicum tuum, occidi. ego te
   non timeo. tu me non terres. tu fortis non es.
15 tu audax non es. veni! pugna! victoria mihi
   facilis erit. ego te mox vincam!'

omnes = everyone
tum = then
forte = by chance

fortissimus, -a, -um
= the bravest
crudelis = cruel

fortis, -e = brave
audax = daring
victoria, -ae, f. =
victory
facilis = easy

Total: 95

Exercise 13.2

1 From the passage give, in Latin, one example of each of the following:

   (a) a verb in the pluperfect tense.   (1)

   (b) an imperative.   (1)

   (c) a personal pronoun.   (1)

   (d) a verb in the future tense.   (1)

2 urbem (line 3). In which case is this noun? Why is this case used?   (2)

3 conspexit (line 6). Give the tense and the 1st person singular of the
   present tense of this verb.   (2)

4 clamavit (line 6). Explain the connection between this word and
   the English word *exclamation*.   (1)

5 verba (line 12). Give the gender of this noun.   (1)

Total: 10

→ omnis, -e = all, every

> Remember: omnes = everyone
>
> omnia = everything

Example

omnes ridebant.   Everybody was laughing.

omnia paravimus.   We prepared everything.

Exercise 13.3

Translate the following into English:

1 rex nobilis.

2 reges nobiles.

3 opus difficile.

4 opera difficilia.

5 milites fortes.

6 omnia scuta.

7 omnes puellae.

8 viri tristes.

9 miles fortis.

10 vulnera crudelia.

11 filius difficilis.

12 iter difficile.

13 domini crudeles.

14 puella tristis.

15 dux nobilis.

2 marks for each question. Total: 30

Exercise 13.4

Translate the following into English:

1 omnia flumina.

2 omnes hastae.

3 dux fortis.

4 duces fortes.

5 feminae crudeles.

6 hostes fortes.

7 opus facile.

8 liber difficilis.

9 viri nobiles.

10 via difficilis.

11 verba crudelia.

12 verbum crudele.

13 servi tristes.

14 nomen nobile.

15 mater tristis.

2 marks for each question. Total: 30

Exercise 13.5

Translate the following into English:

1 dominum crudelem habeo.

2 opus facile facio.

3 omnia vina amo.

4 omnes libros lego.

5 omnes puellas specto.

6 omnia non porto.

7 librum difficilem lego.

8 ducem fortem laudo.

9 servum tristem video.

10 omnes pueros laudo.

3 marks for each question. Total: 30

Exercise 13.6

Translate the following into English:

1 servum fortem libero.

2 omnes puellas amo.

3 omnes non amo.

4 opera difficilia amo.

5 dominum crudelem occido.

6 milites crudeles timeo.

7 milites fortes laudo.

8 opus difficile facio.

9 omnia arma porto.

10 verba crudelia audio.

3 marks for each question. Total: 30

Exercise 13.7

Translate the following into English:

1 hic miles est fortis et validus. (6)

2 hi milites sunt fortes validique. (5)

3 illa puella nobilis est. (4)

4 hic liber difficilis est. (4)

5 dominus meus crudelis est. (4)

6 omnes pueri laborant. (3)

7 cur tristis es, puer? (4)

8 tristis sum quod magister crudelis est. (6)

9 non omnia opera difficilia sunt. (5)

10 hic rex nobilis est. (4)

Total: 45

Exercise 13.8

Translate the following into English:

1 magister crudelis omnes pueros punit. (5)

2 librum facilem legimus. (3)

3 hoc opus difficile non amo. (5)

4 omnes puellae ludunt. (3)

5 non omnes magistri crudeles sunt. (5)

6 servi tristes dominum crudelem timent. (5)

7 dominus nobilis servos laudat. (4)

8 frater meus omnia parat. (4)

9 itinera difficilia saepe facimus. (4)

10 servi tristes sunt quod dominus saepe crudelis est. (7)

Total: 45

Exercise 13.9

Translate the following into Latin:

1 An easy journey.

2 Difficult books.

3 A difficult war.

4 A sad girl.

5 Cruel masters.

6 All the soldiers.

7 Easy work.

8 A brave soldier.

9 Sad women.

10 All wines.

2 marks for each question. Total: 20

Exercise 13.10

Translate the following into Latin:

1 By an easy road.

2 To the cruel boy.

3 For the brave soldiers.

4 Of all the girls.

5 By a cruel wound.

6 For the noble master.

7 With all the spears.

8 Of a brave boy.

9 For the noble girl.

10 By a sad book.

2 marks for each question. Total: 20

Exercise 13.11

Translate the following into Latin:

1 The noble queen was sad. (4)

2 All boys like wine. (4)

3 The cruel king punished the brave soldier. (5)

4 All wars are cruel. (4)

5 The journey was not easy but difficult. (6)

6 The soldiers had fought well. (3)

7 We shall beat all the enemy. (3)

8 All the citizens were afraid. (4)

9 We do not like the cruel master. (4)

10 That king is noble. (4)

11 The wounds of all the citizens are bad. (5)

12 All the pupils have worked well. (4)

13 It is not easy to work well. (5)

14 The brave citizen fought against the enemy. (5)

15 We came to the city by an easy journey. (5)

Total: 65

Exercise 13.12

Put into the plural and translate your answer:

1 ridet. (1 + 1)

2 mater non timebat. (2 + 3)

3 puer patrem habet. (3 + 3)

4 miles urbem oppugnavit. (3 + 3)

5 discipulus magistrum audiebat. (3 + 3)

Total: 25

Exercise 13.13

Put into the singular and translate your answer:

1 sagittae vulnerant. (2 + 2)

2 servi oppida deleverunt. (3 + 3)

3 domini servos puniverunt. (3 + 3)

4 oppida diu defendebamus. (2 + 3)

5 viri currebant. (2 + 2)

Total: 25

Exercise 14.1

Translate the following passage. Line numbers are given on the left. New words are underlined in the text and their meanings given in the margin.

Achilles fights Hector

1 Achilles Hectorem spectabat. Hector
Achillem spectabat. Hector vir fortis et <u>audax</u>
erat. Achilles tamen <u>fortior</u> et <u>audacior</u> <u>quam</u>
Hector erat.

5 subito Hector <u>telum</u> suum iecit. <u>telum</u> ad
Achillem <u>volavit</u>. in scuto tamen Achillis
<u>haesit</u>. Achilles, ubi hoc vidit, risit. deinde
Hectori haec verba crudelia dixit: 'tu me non
occidisti, Hector. ego sum <u>fortior</u> <u>quam</u> tu.
10 ego sum <u>fortissimus</u> omnium Graecorum.
nunc ego te occidam.'

ubi haec dixit, <u>telum</u> ad Hectorem iecit. <u>telum</u>
in corpore Hectoris <u>haesit</u>. Hector ad terram
<u>cecidit</u> mortuus. Achilles <u>laetissimus</u> erat. risit.

audax = bold, daring
fortior = braver
audacior = more daring
quam = than
telum, -i, n. = spear
volo, -are, volavi (1) = I fly
haereo, -ere, haesi (2) = I stick
fortissimus, -a, -um = the bravest

cado, -ere, cecidi (3) = I fall
laetissimus, -a, -um = very happy

Total: 80

Exercise 14.2

1 From the passage give, in Latin, one example of each of the following:

(a) a personal pronoun. (1)

(b) an adjective. (1)

2 spectabat (line 1). Give the Latin subject and the Latin object of this verb. (2)

3 iecit (line 5). Give the person, number and tense of this verb. Give the 1st person singular of the present tense of this verb. (4)

4 Hectorem (line 12). In which case is this noun? Why is this case used? (2)

Total: 10

Exercise 14.3

Translate the following into English:

1 miles fortis.

2 dominus crudelis.

3 templum ingens.

4 pueri felices.

5 magistri sapientes.

6 verba sapientia.

7 dux audax.

8 bellum triste.

9 proelia difficilia.

10 servus felix.

2 marks for each question. Total: 20

→ Adjectives

Exercise 14.4

Translate the following into English:

1 opus ingens.

2 domini difficiles.

3 fratres crudeles.

4 hostes audaces.

5 milites omnes.

6 verba omnia.

7 verbum sapiens.

8 templa ingentia.

9 servi fortes.

10 rex audax.

2 marks for each question. Total: 20

Exercise 14.5

Translate the following into English:

1 dominus crudelis servos omnes punit. (5)

2 omnes milites fortes sunt. (4)

3 non omnia bella sapientia sunt. (5)

4 libros difficiles numquam lego. (4)

5 templum ingens aedificamus. (3)

6 Roma erat urbs ingens. (4)

7 dux sapiens milites fortes semper laudat. (6)

8 non omnes reges crudeles sunt. (5)

9 iter longum et difficile facimus. (5)

10 magister puerum sapientem laudat. (4)

Total: 45

Exercise 14.6

Translate the following into English:

1 omnes milites Romani audaces erant. (5)

2 soror puellae felix est. (4)

3 omnes magistri sapientes sunt. (4)

4 illa puella fratrem sapientem habet. (5)

5 milites ducem felicem semper amant. (5)

6 servi opus difficile faciunt. (4)

7 omnes servi bene laborant. (4)

8 patrem sapientem puellae illius amamus. (5)

9 ad urbem itinere facili venimus. (5)

10 milites omnes mox capiemus. (4)

Total: 45

Exercise 14.7

Translate the following into Latin:

1 That tall soldier is daring. (5)

2 I have a wise father. (3)

3 Soldiers like lucky leaders. (4)

4 Not all men are wise. (5)

5 The enemy were brave. (3)

Total: 20

→ Comparison of adjectives

How to say 'than'

The Latin word for 'than' is **quam**. The nouns being compared are always in the same case.

> **Examples**
>
> puer est sapientior quam puella.   The boy is wiser than the girl.
>
> puellae sunt sapientiores quam pueri.   Girls are wiser than boys.

Exercise 14.8

Translate the following into English:

1 hic miles fortis est; ille miles fortior est. (8)

2 ille miles fortior est quam hic miles. (7)

3 illud telum longum est; hoc telum longius est. (8)

4 hoc telum est longius quam illud. (6)

5 illa puella sapientior est quam hic puer. (7)

6 magistri sapientiores sunt quam pueri. (5)

7 magistri sapientissimi saepe sunt. (4)

8 hoc templum altius est quam illud. (6)

9 hoc opus non facile sed difficillimum est. (7)

10 milites Romani fortiores erant quam milites Graeci. (7)

Total: 65

Exercise 14.9

Translate the following into English:

1 milites audaciores sunt quam cives. (5)

2 illa puella pulcherrima est; puellam pulchriorem numquam vidi. (8)

3 ille magister iratissimus erat; magistrum iratiorem numquam vidi. (8)

4 ille miles audacissimus erat; militem audaciorem numquam vidi. (8)

5 illa mulier tristissima erat; mulierem tristiorem numquam vidi. (8)

6 Achilles miles fortissimus sed crudelissimus erat. (6)

7 Romani audaciores erant quam Graeci. (5)

8 urbes Graecae pulchriores erant quam urbes Romanae. (7)

9 omnes mulieres sapientiores sunt quam viri. (6)

10 Romani clari erant, sed Graeci clariores quam Romani erant. (9)

Total: 70

Exercise 14.10

Translate the following into Latin:

1 A very wise man.

2 A very high wall.

3 Very daring soldiers.

4 A very fortunate king.

5 A very cruel master.

6 Very long rivers.

7 A very difficult journey.

8 A very dear wife.

9 A very sacred temple.

10 Very easy tasks.

2 marks for each question. Total: 20

Exercise 14.11

Translate the following into Latin:

1 With very happy words.

2 On the higher wall.

3 To the very angry teacher.

4 For the very lucky boys.

5 Of a wiser man.

6 With a more beautiful girl.

7 For the very famous king.

8 Of very cruel masters.

9 For a very long war.

10 By an easier journey.

2 marks for each question. Total: 20

Chapter 14

Exercise 14.12

Translate the following into Latin:

1 My son is very tall and very famous.   (6)

2 Marcus is wiser than Flavia.   (5)

3 Boys are wiser than girls.   (5)

4 That temple is taller than this.   (6)

5 I am looking at very beautiful girls.   (3)

Total: 25

Exercise 14.13

Put into the plural and translate your answer:

1 dedit.   (1 + 1)

2 magnum telum habeo.   (3 + 3)

3 miles audax est.   (3 + 3)

4 vir non festinabit.   (2 + 3)

5 iuvenis gladium habebat.   (3 + 3)

Total: 25

Exercise 14.14

Put into the singular and translate your answer:

1 non curremus.   (1 + 2)

2 servi felices erant.   (3 + 3)

3 hastae milites vulneraverunt.   (3 + 3)

4 iuvenes tela timebant.   (3 + 3)

5 itinera longa et difficilia sunt.   (4 + 5)

Total: 30

Exercise 14.15

Give and translate the following verb parts:

1 The 2nd person singular, imperfect tense of eo.

2 The 1st person plural, present tense of vinco.

3 The 3rd person plural, perfect tense of vulnero.

4 The 3rd person singular, pluperfect tense of maneo.

5 The 1st person singular, perfect tense of discedo.

2 marks for each question. Total: 10

Exercise 14.16

Give the translation, person, number, tense and 1st person singular of the present tense of the following:

1 ruis.

2 occupant.

3 accipiebat.

4 defendent.

5 vicerat.

5 marks for each question. Total: 25

Exercise 14.17

Translate the following into Latin:

1 That leader was daring. (4)

2 I have a lucky friend. (3)

3 The leader threw many missiles. (4)

4 Wise men often fear death. (5)

5 Many missiles wounded the leader. (4)

Total: 20

Exercise 14.18

Translate the following into Latin:

1 The missiles of the enemy were long.

2 The walls of the town were huge.

3 We attacked the city with many missiles.

4 The courage of the citizen frightened the king.

5 The soldiers' courage was great.

4 marks for each question. Total: 20

Exercise 15.1

Translate the following passage. Line numbers are given on the left. New words are underlined in the text and their meanings given in the margin.

Achilles mistreats Hector's body

1 Achilles vir crudelissimus erat. corpus Hectoris
curruĭ suo pedibus vinxit. deinde currum
circum muros Troiae egit, corpus Hectoris
trahens. omnes cives Troiani, ubi hoc viderunt,
5 tristissimi erant.

Paris filius Priami erat. frater igitur Hectoris
erat. quod Achilles Hectorem occiderat,
iratissimus erat. arma cepit, ex urbe cucurrit,
in proelium ruit. Achillem mox invenit. haec
10 verba ei dixit: 'Achilles, vir pessimus es. nemo
peior est quam tu. Hectorem, fratrem meum,
occidisti. ego tamen miles melior sum quam
tu. numquam effugies. nemo te servare
poterit. te nunc occidam.' Paris telum in
15 Achillem misit. telum in calce Achillis haesit.
Achilles ad terram mortuus cecidit.

currui = dative of currus = chariot
pes, pedis, m. = foot
vincio, -ire, vinxi (4) = I tie
circum + acc. = around
ago, -ere, egi (3) = I drive
trahens = dragging
Priamus, -i, m. = Priam (a name)
invenio, -ire, inveni (4) = I find
pessimus, -a, -um = very wicked
peior = more wicked
melior = better
effugio, -ere, effugi (3½) = I escape
servo, -are, servavi (1) = I save
poterit = will be able
calx, calcis, f. = heel
haereo, -ere, haesi (2) = I stick
cado, -ere, cecidi (3) = I fall

Total: 100

Exercise 15.2

1 From the passage give, in Latin, one example of each of the following:

(a) a superlative adjective. (1)

(b) a preposition. (1)

(c) a verb in the pluperfect tense. (1)

(d) an adverb. (1)

2 occiderat (line 7). Give the Latin subject and the Latin object of this verb. (2)

3 urbe (line 8). In which case is this noun? Why is this case used? (2)

4 misit (line 15). Give the tense and the 1st person singular of the present tense of this verb. (2)

Total: 10

→ Irregular comparison

Exercise 15.3

Translate the following into English:

1 ego sum puer bonus, sed tu es melior. (8)

2 Sextus puer pessimus est. (4)

3 Iulius Caesar erat dux optimus. (5)

4 hoc templum est maius quam illud. (6)

5 Alexander Magnus miles melior erat quam Iulius Caesar. (8)

6 cibus matris tuae optimus erat. (5)

7 naves maximae appropinquabant. (3)

8 ego plus pecuniae habeo quam tu. (6)

9 Italia maior est quam Britannia. (5)

10 Britannia minor est quam Italia. (5)

Total: 55

Exercise 15.4

Translate the following into English:

1 illa puella minima est. (4)

2 hic puer maior quam illa puella est. (7)

3 plurimi milites oppidum oppugnaverunt. (4)

4 ille magister pessimus erat. (4)

5 puellae meliores sunt quam pueri. (5)

6 pueri peiores sunt quam puellae. (5)

7 milites Romani optimi erant. (4)

8 Romani milites meliores quam Graeci habebant. (6)

9 Graeci milites peiores quam Romani habebant. (6)

10 cives plurimi maximum oppidum defendebant. (5)

Total: 50

Exercise 15.5

Translate the following into English:

1 vulnus meum pessimum est. (4)

2 vulnus peius numquam accepi. (4)

3 montes Italiae maiores sunt quam montes Britanniae. (7)

4 muri Troiae olim maximi erant. (5)

5 milites in maximo periculo erant. (5)

6 hic agricola plurimos et maximos agros habet. (7)

7 sunt in agris plurimi equi. (5)

8 in maiore nave quam illa numquam fui. (7)

9 Graeci templa maiora et meliora quam Romani aedificabant. (8)

10 templa Romanorum minora et peiora quam Graecorum erant. (8)

Total: 60

Exercise 15.6

Translate the following into Latin:

1 A very bad boy.

2 Very good pupils.

3 Very many soldiers.

4 Very many ships.

5 Very good leaders.

6 A bigger temple.

7 A very small city.

8 Very big wars.

9 Smaller girls.

10 A very good teacher.

2 marks for each question: Total: 20

Exercise 15.7

Translate the following into Latin:

1 Not all teachers are very good. (5)

2 I have a few very bad pupils. (4)

3 We are carrying very big shields. (3)

4 That girl was very small. (4)

5 I have never seen a bigger ship. (4)

Total: 20

Exercise 15.8

Translate the following into English:

1 magister optimus.

2 flumen altissimum.

3 discipulus pessimus.

4 miles fortissimus.

5 milites fortissimi.

6 puella pulcherrima.

7 maximum oppidum.

8 plurimi pueri.

9 maxima turba.

10 flumen minimum.

11 hostes audacissimi.

12 servi pessimi.

13 liber difficillimus.

14 dominus crudelissimus.

15 vir nobilissimus.

16 vinum optimum.

17 milites optimi.

18 liber longissimus.

19 liber optimus.

20 flumina longissima.

2 marks for each question. Total: 40

Exercise 15.9

Translate the following into English:

1 uxor pulcherrima.

2 verba sapientissima.

3 naves maximae.

4 hostes saevissimi.

5 mulieres pulcherrimae.

6 corpora maxima.

7 templa maxima.

8 templum maximum.

9 scutum maximum.

10 pueri laetissimi.

11 plurimae feminae.

12 aqua altissima.

13 puer felicissimus.

14 femina saevissima.

15 copiae maximae.

16 via longissima.

17 vir pulcherrimus.

18 caelum pulcherrimum.

19 ager maximus.

20 magister iratissimus.

2 marks for each question. Total: 40

Exercise 15.10

Put into the plural and translate your answer:

1 effugiebat. (1 + 1)

2 miles pugnabat. (2 + 2)

3 librum meum tandem inveni. (3 + 4)

4 civis tutus est. (3 + 3)

5 puella iuvenem timebat. (3 + 3)

Total: 25

Exercise 15.11

Put into the singular and translate your answer:

1 defenditis. (1 + 1)

2 naves veniebant. (2 + 2)

3 servi effugerunt. (2 + 2)

4 cives urbes servabant. (3 + 3)

5 corpora invenerunt. (2 + 2)

Total: 20

Exercise 15.12

Translate the following into English:

1 plurimi servi hostes timebant et ex urbe effugiebant. (8)
2 Romani opera difficiliora quam Graeci faciebant. (6)
3 quamquam dux multos hostes vicerat, nemo eum laudavit. (8)
4 omnes milites mortem in bello timent. (6)
5 cives Graeci sapientiores erant quam cives Romani. (7)
6 milites Romani multa oppida ceperant et multos hostes vicerant. (9)
7 plurimas puellas pulcherrimas in urbe heri conspexi. (7)
8 milites Romani pro civibus Romanis semper fortiter pugnabant. (8)
9 hi servi dominum crudelissimum habebant. eum non amabant. (8)
10 cives muros oppidi contra hostes maxima virtute defendebant. (8)

Total: 75

Exercise 15.13

Translate the following into Latin:

1 I am running around the wall. (3)
2 I found money in the street. (4)
3 The lucky slaves escaped. (3)
4 The king saved much money. (4)
5 The leader seized the town. (3)
6 The huge wall saved the city. (4)
7 The Romans conquered the Greeks with weapons. (4)
8 The farmer found a horse in the field. (5)
9 The weapons of the Romans frightened the enemy. (4)
10 The brave soldier saves his friend in the battle. (6)

Total: 40

Exercise 16.1

Translate the following passage. Line numbers are given on the left. New words are underlined in the text and their meanings given in the margin.

The Greeks despair of taking Troy, but Ulysses comes up with a plan

1   diu Graeci urbem Troiam oppugnaverant. <u>post</u>
    multos <u>annos</u> fessi erant. quamquam fortiter
    pugnabant, urbem capere non <u>poterant</u>. 'quid
    faciemus?' <u>inquiunt</u>. '<u>num</u> urbem capiemus?
5   muri Troiae altissimi et maximi sunt. eos
    delere numquam <u>poterimus</u>. <u>domum</u> redire
    debemus.'

    Ulixes, miles audacissimus Graecorum, ubi
    haec verba audivit, iratus erat. magna <u>voce</u>
10 clamavit: 'audite me, Graeci! <u>nolite stulti</u> esse!
    nos Graeci sapientiores quam illi Troiani
    sumus. <u>domum</u> redire non debetis! Troiam
    mox capiemus. <u>consilium</u> habeo. <u>consilium</u>
    optimum habeo. <u>consilio</u> meo urbem
15 delebimus. equum <u>ligneum</u> maximum
    aedificate!' Graeci igitur equum ligneum
    maximum aedificaverunt.

post + acc. = after
annus, -i, m. = year
poterant = they were able
inquiunt = they said
num *introduces a question which expects the answer 'no'*; surely ... not?
poterimus = we will be able
domum = home
vox, vocis f. = voice
nolite + infinitive = don't ...!
stultus, -a, -um = stupid
consilium, -i, n. = plan

ligneus, -a, -um = wooden

Total: 85

Exercise 16.2

1   From the passage give, in Latin, one example of each of the following:

    (a) a superlative adjective.   (1)

    (b) a comparative adjective.   (1)

    (c) an imperative.   (1)

    (d) an adverb.   (1)

2   urbem (line 1). In which case is this noun? Why is this case used?   (2)

3   muri (line 5). Give the gender of this noun.   (1)

4   capiemus (line 13). Give the person, number and tense of this verb. (3)

Total: 10

→ possum, posse, potui = I am able, I can

Remember: The verb possum is preceded by an infinitive.

Examples

puella currere non potest.	= The girl is not able to run.
	= The girl cannot run.
ille miles bene pugnare poterat.	= That soldier was able to fight well.
	= That soldier could fight well.

Exercise 16.3

Translate the following into English:

1 potest.

2 potestis.

3 poterat.

4 potuerat.

5 poterit.

6 potuimus.

7 posse.

8 potueras.

9 poteras.

10 potes.

11 possum.

12 poteramus.

13 potuit.

14 potuerunt.

15 potueramus.

16 possunt.

17 poterunt.

18 possumus.

19 potuistis.

20 potero.

1 mark for each question. Total: 20

Exercise 16.4

Translate the following into English:

1 laborare non possum. (2)

2 effugere potest. (2)

3 vincere possumus. (2)

4 exspectare non poteram. (3)

5 fugere poterant. (2)

6 redire non possum. (3)

7 currere non poteramus. (3)

8 oppugnare potuerunt. (2)

9 dormire non possum. (3)

10 pugnare non poteras. (3)

Total: 25

Exercise 16.5

Translate the following into English:

1 nautae ad insulam navigare poterant. (5)

2 hostes vincere numquam poterimus. (4)

3 milites urbem delere non poterant. (5)

4 servi ex oppido effugere non poterant. (6)

5 milites hoc oppidum capere poterunt. (5)

6 Romani tela iacere non poterant. (5)

7 ille rex bene regere non potest. (6)

8 cives urbem bene defendere non poterant. (6)

9 ille servus hoc vinum bibere non potest. (7)

10 ad urbem hodie venire non potuimus. (6)

Total: 55

Exercise 16.6

Translate the following into English:

1 quis ad templum cras venire poterit? (6)

2 hoc iter longum facere numquam poterimus. (6)

3 milites hoc flumen transire non possunt. (6)

4 dominus illum servum liberare non poterat. (6)

5 comites celeriter currere non poterant. (5)

6 magistri omnia facere non possunt. (5)

7 Graeci Romanos in hoc proelio vincere non poterant. (8)

8 hic vir librum longum scribere non poterit. (7)

9 multam pecuniam filio meo dare non poteram. (7)

10 milites fessi contra hos hostes bene pugnare non poterant. (9)

Total: 65

Exercise 16.7

Translate the following into Latin:

1 I can read. (2)

2 We could not escape. (3)

3 You (sing.) cannot laugh. (3)

4 I will not be able to work. (3)

5 They could not attack. (3)

6 I can sail. (2)

7 He could sing. (2)

8 They will be able to come. (2)

9 They could not see. (3)

10 You (pl.) can depart. (2)

Total: 25

Exercise 16.8

Translate the following into Latin:

1 This boy cannot drink wine.

2 The citizens will not be able to defend the town.

3 The pupils have not been able to do this.

4 The enemy could not find the citizens' money.

5 The leader could not prepare very big forces.

5 marks for each question. Total: 25

Exercise 16.9

Put into the plural and translate your answer:

1 mox ex urbe effugiam. (3 + 4)

2 rex nobilis est. (3 + 3)

3 urbem defendam. (2 + 2)

4 puellam videras. (2 + 2)

5 amicum exspectabat. (2 + 2)

Total: 25

Exercise 16.10

Put into the singular and translate your answer:

1 servi currunt.

2 amici effugiebant.

3 hostes invenistis.

4 milites servaveramus.

5 tela habebamus.

2 + 2 marks for each question. Total: 20

Exercise 16.11

Put into the plural and translate your answer:

1 it.   (1 + 1)
2 oppidum numquam aedificavi.   (2 + 3)
3 puer puellam amabat.   (3 + 3)
4 dux militem fessum defendebat.   (4 + 4)
5 fortiter pugnabo.   (2 + 2)

Total: 25

Exercise 16.12

Put into the singular and translate your answer:

1 rediimus.   (1 + 1)
2 illi cives effugiebant.   (3 + 3)
3 muri ingentes erant.   (3 + 3)
4 discipuli bene laboraverunt.   (2 + 3)
5 mulieres templa spectabant.   (3 + 3)

Total: 25

Exercise 16.13

Give and translate the following verb parts:

1 The 3rd person singular, present tense of **possum**.
2 The 2nd person plural, future tense of **servo**.
3 The 3rd person plural, perfect tense of **invenio**.
4 The 1st person plural, perfect tense of **eo**.
5 The 2nd person singular, imperfect tense of **vinco**.

2 marks for each question. Total: 10

Exercise 16.14

Give the translation, person, number and 1st person singular of the present tense of the following:

1 poterat.
2 festinabamus.
3 effugient.
4 eramus.
5 peribat.

4 marks for each question. Total: 20

Exercise 16.15

Translate the following into Latin:

1 That wound was cruel. (4)

2 We fear the missiles of the enemy. (3)

3 They attacked our city with missiles. (4)

4 The enemy were noble. (3)

5 The journey is not long but difficult. (6)

Total: 20

Exercise 16.16

Translate the following into Latin:

1 The king escaped from the city.

2 The enemy attacked the smallest island.

3 The Romans were able to fight well.

4 The sailors sailed to the island.

5 By the courage of the soldiers we took the town.

4 marks for each question. Total: 20

Exercise 17.1

Translate the following passage. Line numbers are given on the left. New words are underlined in the text and their meanings given in the margin.

The Trojans see the horse

1 Graeci equum <u>ligneum</u> maximum
aedificaverant. <u>antequam</u> in navibus
discesserunt, plurimos milites in equum
posuerunt et equum in <u>litore</u> prope urbem
5 <u>reliquerunt</u>.

Troiani, ubi equum viderunt, e <u>portis</u>
exierunt. <u>attoniti</u> erant. diu equum
spectabant. unus e Troianis haec verba dixit:
'Graeci discesserunt. <u>nonne</u> eos vicimus? hic
10 equus donum nobis est. eum in <u>mediam</u>
urbem <u>trahere</u> debetis, cives!'

Troianus secundus autem magna voce
clamavit: '<u>num</u> hic equus donum est? Graeci
dona numquam dant. Graeci <u>homines</u> <u>fallaces</u>
15 sunt. <u>nolite</u> equum in urbem <u>trahere</u>, cives!
eum delere debemus!'

tandem Troiani equum in urbem <u>trahere</u>
constituerunt.

ligneus, -a, -um = wooden
antequam = before
litus, litoris, n. = shore
relinquo, -ere, reliqui (3) = I
leave behind, I abandon

porta, -ae, f. = gate
attonitus, -a, -um = amazed
nonne *introduces a question
which expects the answer
'yes'*; surely...?
medius, -a, -um = the middle of
traho, -ere, traxi (3) = I pull,
I drag
num *introduces a question
which expects the answer
'no'*; surely ... not?
homo, hominis, m./f. = person;
plural: people
fallax, fallacis = deceitful
nolite + infinitive = don't ...!

Total: 90

Exercise 17.2

1 From the passage give, in Latin, one example of each of the following:

(a) a verb in the pluperfect tense. (1)

(b) a preposition. (1)

(c) an ordinal number. (1)

(d) an imperative. (1)

2 equum (line 1). Explain the connection between this word and the English
word *equestrian*. (1)

3 navibus (line 2). In which case is this noun? Why is this case used? (2)

4 posuerunt (line 4). Give the 1st person singular of the present tense
of this verb. (1)

5 viderunt (line 6). Give the Latin subject and the Latin object of this verb. (2)

Total: 10

→ Prohibitions

Examples

noli currere, puer!   Do not run, boy! (sing. prohibition)

nolite currere, pueri!   Do not run, boys! (pl. prohibition)

Exercise 17.3

Translate the following into English:

1 noli ridere, puer!

2 nolite ridere, pueri!

3 nolite oppugnare, milites!

4 nolite effugere, servi!

5 noli exspectare, amice!

6 noli inire, iuvenis!

7 nolite navigare, nautae!

8 noli stare, pater!

9 nolite ludere, puellae!

10 noli discedere, mater!

3 marks for each question. Total: 30

Exercise 17.4

Translate the following into English:

1 noli flere, femina!   (3)

2 nolite libros scribere, poetae!   (4)

3 noli currere, miles!   (3)

4 noli sedere, puella!   (3)

5 nolite timere, comites!   (3)

6 nolite hic manere, cives!   (4)

7 nolite pugnare, pueri mali!   (4)

8 noli festinare, serve!   (3)

9 nolite cantare, filiae!   (3)

10 nolite me hic relinquere, amici!   (5)

Total: 35

Exercise 17.5

Translate the following into English:

1 nolite oppidum oppugnare, milites!   (4)

2 nolite verba magistri audire, pueri!   (5)

3 noli iter longum facere, amice!   (5)

4 nolite urbem contra hostes defendere, cives!   (6)

5 noli hunc servum punire, domine! (5)

6 nolite illos servos liberare, domini! (5)

7 noli e templo exire, puer! (5)

8 noli pecuniam patri tradere, iuvenis! (5)

9 nolite in via stare, puellae! (5)

10 noli hoc vinum bibere, mater! (5)

Total: 50

Exercise 17.6

Translate the following into Latin:

1 Don't run, girls!

2 Don't approach, boy!

3 Don't charge, soldiers!

4 Don't return, friend!

5 Don't work, pupils!

6 Don't fight, comrades!

7 Don't attack, slaves!

8 Don't hurry, mother!

9 Don't reply, boys!

10 Don't fight, citizens!

3 marks for each question. Total: 30

Exercise 17.7

Translate the following into Latin:

1 Don't play in the road, boy! (5)

2 Don't wound the enemy, soldiers! (4)

3 Don't set free this slave, master! (5)

4 Don't cross the river, sailor! (4)

5 Don't listen to that teacher, pupils! (5)

6 Don't hand over the money, king! (4)

7 Don't attack the city, Romans! (4)

8 Don't throw your spears, slaves! (5)

9 Don't kill the king, slave! (4)

10 Don't drink all the wine, girl! (5)

Total: 45

→ nonne and num

Exercise 17.8

Translate the following into English:

1 flet. (1)

2 num flet? (2)

3 nonne flet? (2)

4 pugnant. (1)

5 pugnantne? (1)

6 num pugnant? (2)

7 effugerunt. (1)

8 effugeruntne? (1)

9 nonne effugerunt? (2)

10 num effugerunt? (2)

Total: 15

Exercise 17.9

Translate the following into English:

1 bene pugnabat. (2)

2 nonne bene pugnabat? (3)

3 num bene pugnabat? (3)

4 hic miles fortis est. (4)

5 nonne hic miles fortis est? (5)

6 num hic miles fortis est? (5)

7 Hector miles audax erat. (4)

8 nonne Hector audax erat? (4)

9 num Hector miles audax erat? (5)

10 num Hector fortissimus Troianorum erat? (5)

Total: 40

Exercise 17.10

Translate the following into English:

1 nonne cives urbem bene defendebant? (5)

2 num puer hoc fecit? (4)

3 num Graeci Romanos vicerunt? (4)

4 num omnes mortem timent? (4)

5 nonne illam puellam in urbe heri conspexisti? (7)

6 nonne matrem tuam amas? (4)

7 nonne Graeci multa arma collegerunt? (5)

8 num femina hoc facere poterit? (5)

9 nonne milites Romani in bello bene pugnaverunt? (7)

10 num hoc facere difficile est? (5)

Total: 50

Exercise 17.11

Translate the following into Latin:

1 We are Romans, aren't we? (3)

2 We are not Romans, are we? (3)

3 Are we Romans? (2)

4 You (sing.) are not running, are you? (2)

5 Are you (sing.) running? (1)

6 You (sing.) are running, aren't you? (2)

7 You (sing.) weren't laughing, were you? (2)

8 You (sing.) were laughing, weren't you? (2)

9 Were you (sing.) laughing? (1)

10 We won't escape, will we? (2)

Total: 20

Exercise 17.12

Translate the following into Latin:

1 This man is not very wise, is he?

2 These weapons are good, aren't they?

3 That journey isn't easy, is it?

4 You (sing.) saw that unhappy girl, didn't you?

5 We will attack this city tomorrow, won't we?

5 marks for each question. Total: 25

Exercise 17.13

Translate the following into Latin:

1 The man does not love his wife, does he?

2 The Romans will beat the enemy, won't they?

3 We won't be able to do this, will we?

4 That soldier received a wound, didn't he?

5 Death will come to everyone, won't it?

4 marks for each question. Total: 20

Exercise 17.14

Put into the plural and translate your answer:

1	clamo.	(1 + 1)
2	regina adveniebat.	(2 + 2)
3	puellam heri conspexi.	(2 + 3)
4	mulier optimam cenam parabat.	(4 + 4)
5	dux amicum reliquit.	(3 + 3)

Total: 25

Exercise 17.15

Put into the singular and translate your answer:

1	colligebamus.	(1 + 1)
2	voces semper audiunt.	(2 + 3)
3	milites bene pugnaverunt.	(2 + 3)
4	discipuli comites non habebant.	(3 + 4)
5	cives duces audiebant.	(3 + 3)

Total: 25

Exercise 17.16

Translate the following into Latin:

1 My daughter has a good voice. (5)

2 He is a wise man. (3)

3 Many men are not wise. (5)

4 The Romans will attack tomorrow. (3)

5 Do not leave the money there! (4)

Total: 20

Chapter 17

Exercise 17.17

Translate the following into Latin:

1   We are listening to the voices of those girls. (4)

2   The boys are standing in the middle of the road. (5)

3   He left much money in the road. (5)

4   The citizens left their weapons in the city. (5)

5   All Roman soldiers had great courage. (6)

Total: 25

Exercise 17.18

Translate the following into English:

1   hostes vicimus. (2)

2   librum scripsit. (2)

3   multam pecuniam invenerunt. (3)

4   servi effugerunt. (2)

5   tela iecerunt. (2)

6   poeta cras veniet. (3)

7   vulnus accepit. (2)

8   pater meus discessit. (3)

9   ex urbe exierunt. (3)

10 illud verbum dixit. (3)

Total: 25

Exercise 18.1

Translate the following passage. Line numbers are given on the left. New words are underlined in the text and their meanings given in the margin.

The fall of Troy

1 Troiani equum in urbem traxerunt. laetissimi
  erant quod Graeci discesserant. laetissimi
  erant quod Graecos vicerant.

  illa nocte igitur omnes cives festum
5 celebrabant. multum cibi consumebant et
  multum vini bibebant. mox omnes Troiani
  dormiebant.

  media nocte milites Graeci, qui in equo erant,
  de equo silentio descenderunt. subito ad
10 Troianos dormientes magnis clamoribus
  ruerunt. Troiani se defendere non poterant.
  multi Troiani gladiis Graecorum perierunt.
  inter hos erat Priamus senex, rex Troiae.
  Graeci paucos Troianos vivos reliquerunt.

15 sic Graeci post decem annos urbem Troiam
  dolo ceperunt. maximam partem urbis
  deleverunt. Helenam ad Graeciam reducere
  nunc poterant.

traho, -ere, traxi (3) = I drag
nox, noctis, f. = night
festum celebro, -are, -avi (1)
= I hold a celebration
qui = who
silentio = in silence
descendo, -ere, descendi (3)
= I climb down
dormientes = as they were
sleeping
clamor, clamoris, m. = shout
se = themselves
senex, -is, m. = old man
pauci, -ae, -a = few
vivus, -a, -um = alive
annus, -i, m. = year
dolus, -i, m. = trickery
pars, partis, f. = part
Graecia, -ae, f. = Greece
reduco, -ere, reduxi (3) = I
lead back

Total: 90

Exercise 18.2

1 From the passage give, in Latin, an example of:

  (a) a superlative adjective. (1)

  (b) a verb in the imperfect tense. (1)

  (c) a preposition followed by a noun in the accusative case. (1)

  (d) an infinitive. (1)

2 vicerant (line 3). Give the person, number and tense of this verb. Give the
  1st person singular of the present tense of this verb. (4)

3 urbem (line 15). Give the case of this noun. Why is this case used? (2)

Total: 10

→ Reflexive pronouns

Examples

me necabo.	I will kill myself.
se amat.	He loves himself.
se defendunt.	They defend themselves.

Note: secum (sing.)   with him/with her
secum (pl.)   with them

Exercise 18.3

Translate the following into English:

1 ille puer se amat.   (4)

2 Romani se necare constituerunt.   (4)

3 Troiani se defendere paraverunt.   (4)

4 illa puella se semper spectat.   (5)

5 dux milites iter secum facere iussit.   (6)

6 discipuli sapientes se numquam laudant.   (5)

7 cives Troiani se fortiter defendebant.   (5)

8 ille miles se gladio suo vulneravit.   (6)

9 cives tristes hostibus se tradiderunt.   (5)

10 multae feminae in flumine se spectabant.   (6)

Total: 50

Exercise 18.4

Translate the following into English:

1 num hic senex mortuus est?   (5)

2 multi perierunt, pauci effugerunt.   (4)

3 nolite me relinquere, comites!   (4)

4 clamores multorum senum audivimus.   (5)

5 hi milites fortes se servare cupiunt.   (6)

6 bene pugnate, cives!   (3)

7 Graeci non fortiores sunt quam nos.   (6)

8 nonne milites Graeci felicissimi erant?   (5)

9 vos tuti estis, nos in magno periculo sumus.   (8)

10 quis nos servare poterit?   (4)

Total: 50

Exercise 18.5

Translate the following into English:

1 senex et fortis et audax erat. (6)

2 num ille puer in media via stat? (7)

3 non omnes cives fortes erant. (5)

4 ille dux hoc oppidum capere numquam poterit. (7)

5 hostes flumen transire non poterant. (5)

6 milites ducem felicem semper amant. (5)

7 pater meus vocem magnam habet. (5)

8 Graeci, ubi Troiam ceperunt, Helenam ad Graeciam reduxerunt. (8)

9 nonne Troiani urbem suam bene defendebant? (6)

10 clamores illarum feminarum perterritarum magni erant. (6)

Total: 60

Exercise 18.6

Translate the following into English:

1 dei deaeque, ubi deam Discordiam viderunt, iratissimi erant. (9)

2 Menelaus, ubi Paris Helenam cepit, nuntios ad omnes comites misit. (10)

3 Graeci, ubi de Helena audiverunt, copias ad Menelaum miserunt. (9)

4 copiae Graecorum, ubi trans mare navigaverunt, Troiam oppugnaverunt. (8)

5 Achilles, ubi Hectorem occidit, laetus erat. (6)

6 Graeci, ubi equum magnum aedificaverunt, eum prope urbem reliquerunt. (9)

7 Graeci, ubi equum prope urbem reliquerunt, discesserunt. (7)

8 Troiani, ubi equum viderunt, timebant. (5)

9 multi Troiani, ubi Graecos in media urbe viderunt, fugerunt. (9)

10 Graeci, ubi urbem Troiam deleverunt, ad Graeciam redierunt. (8)

Total: 80

Exercise 18.7

Translate the following into English:

1 hic vir, quamquam nauta est, aquam timet. (7)

2 Achilles, quamquam miles audax erat, pugnare non cupiebat. (8)

3 Graeci, quamquam Troiam diu oppugnaverunt, urbem armis capere non poterant. (10)

4 Graeci, quamquam milites meliores erant quam Troiani, non bene pugnaverunt. (10)

5 ego, quamquam sapientior sum quam multi homines, multam pecuniam non habeo. (10)

6 Troiani, quamquam urbem bene defenderunt, eam servare non poterant. (9)

7 miles, quamquam fessus erat, diu pugnavit. (6)

8 discipuli, quamquam magister sapientissimus erat, eum non amabant. (8)

9 quamquam vox senis magna erat, eam audire non poteramus. (9)

10 cives, quamquam hostes timebant, contra eos bene pugnaverunt. (8)

Total: 85

Exercise 18.8

Put into the plural and translate your answer:

1 audis. (1 + 1)

2 senex non timebat. (2 + 3)

3 telum longum erat. (3 + 3)

4 agricola equum habet. (3 + 3)

5 iuvenis hastam tenebat. (3 + 3)

Total: 25

Exercise 18.9

Put into the singular and translate your answer:

1 possumus. (1 + 1)

2 puellas reduxerunt. (2 + 2)

3 clamores hominum audivimus. (3 + 3)

4 discipuli non responderunt. (2 + 3)

5 milites proelia non saepe timebant. (3 + 5)

Total: 25

Exercise 18.10

Give and translate the following verb parts:

1 The 1st person plural, future tense of reduco.

2 The 3rd person plural, imperfect tense of relinquo.

3 The 3rd person singular, imperfect tense of possum.

4 The 1st person singular, perfect tense of conspicio.

5 The 2nd person plural, present tense of bibo.

2 marks for each question. Total: 10

Exercise 18.11

Translate, then give the person, number, tense and 1st person singular of the present tense of the following:

1 posuit.

2 potuit.

3 reduxerunt.

4 effugisti.

5 relinquemus.

5 marks for each question. Total: 25

Exercise 18.12

Translate the following into Latin:

1 Many citizens were alive, weren't they? (4)

2 Few women were staying in the city. (5)

3 Don't be afraid, friends! I will be able to do this. (6)

4 Old men are wiser than young men. (5)

5 We slaves all have very cruel masters. (5)

Total: 25

Exercise 18.13

Translate the following into Latin:

1 Both men and women have loud voices. (7)

2 That soldier is more daring than this one. (6)

3 Surely Achilles was not the bravest soldier of the Greeks? (6)

4 The Trojans put the horse in the middle of the city. (6)

5 Wise men often like difficult tasks. (5)

Total: 30

Exercise 18.14

Keeping the same person and number, put the following verbs into the imperfect tense and translate your answer:

1 servavit.

2 viderunt.

3 superavi.

4 aedificavimus.

5 steterunt.

6 timuerunt.

7 delevistis.

8 spectavit.

9 responderunt.

10 amavit.

2 marks for each question. Total: 20

Test exercises

Test 1: The story of Perseus (1)

1 Translate the following passage into good English:

Acrisius gets a warning

1 Acrisius rex clarus erat. <u>urbem</u> Argos regebat.
  filiam <u>unam</u> habebat. <u>nomen</u> filiae Danae erat.
  olim dei Acrisio nuntiaverunt: '<u>cave</u>, Acrisi!
  filia tua filium <u>habebit</u>. <u>hic</u> filius te necabit.'
5 <u>haec</u> verba Acrisium terruerunt.

urbs, urbis, f. = city
unam = one
nomen = name
cave! = beware!
habebit = (she) will have
hic = this
necabit = (he) will kill
haec = these

(30)

2 (a) erat (line 1). Give the 1st person singular of the
       present tense of this verb. (1)

  (b) regebat (line 1). Give the person of this verb. (1)

  (c) Acrisio (line 3). Give the case of this noun. (1)

  (d) terruerunt (line 5). Give the number of this verb. (1)

3 Using the vocabulary given below, translate the following sentences into Latin:

  (a) I had a famous daughter. (3)

  (b) The words frighten the son. (3)

I have	habeo, -ere (2)
famous	clarus, -a, -um
daughter	filia, -ae, f.
word	verbum, -i, n.
I frighten	terreo, -ere (2)
son	filius, -i, m.

Total: 40

Test 2: The story of Perseus (2)

1   Translate the following passage into good English:

Acrisius tries to play safe

1   Acrisius verba deorum timebat. magnam igitur
    turrim aedificare constituit. ubi hoc fecit, filiam,
    Danaen nomine, in turrim posuit. deinde servos
    Danaen custodire iussit. 'sic tutus ero,' inquit
5   Acrisius. tutus tamen non erat.

turrim, f. = tower
Danaen = the accusative
case of Danae (Greek form)
nomine = by name
custodio, -ire, -ivi (4) =
I guard
ero = I shall be

(30)

2   (a) verba (line 1). Give the gender of this noun. (1)

    (b) deorum (line 1). Give the case of this noun. (1)

    (c) fecit (line 2). Give the 1st person singular of the present
        tense of this verb. (1)

    (d) Give an example from the passage of an infinitive. (1)

3   Using the vocabulary given below, translate the following sentences into Latin:

    (a) The daughter was afraid of the god. (3)

    (b) The god frightens the slaves. (3)

daughter	filia, -ae, f.
I am afraid of	timeo, -ere (2)
god	deus, -i, m.
I frighten	terreo, -ere (2)
slave	servus, -i, m.

Total: 40

Test 3: The story of Perseus (3)

1   Translate the following passage into good English:

Jupiter pays Danae a visit

1   Iuppiter rex deorum erat. quamquam Iuno, regina
    deorum, uxor <u>eius</u> erat, multas alias feminas saepe
    amabat. postquam <u>Danaen</u> pulchram vidit, <u>eam</u>
    quoque amare constituit. in <u>turrim</u> igitur intravit
5   et Danaen amavit.

eius = his
Danaen = the accusative case of Danae (Greek form)
eam = her
turrim, f. = tower

(30)

2   (a) erat (line 1). Give the 1st person singular of the
        present tense of this verb.   (1)

    (b) feminas (line 2). Give the case of this noun.   (1)

    (c) Give an example from the passage of a preposition.   (1)

    (d) vidit (line 3). Give the person of this verb.   (1)

3   Using the vocabulary given below, translate the following sentences into Latin:

    (a) The woman liked the queen.   (3)

    (b) The queen sees the god.   (3)

woman	femina, -ae, f.
I like	amo, -are (1)
queen	regina, -ae, f.
I see	video, -ere (2)
god	deus, -i, m.

Total: 40

1   Translate the following passage into good English:

Acrisius makes a worrying discovery

1   postea Danae filium parvum <u>peperit</u>. nomen pueri
     Perseus erat. Acrisius, ubi Perseum vidit, perterritus
     et iratus erat. clamavit: 'quis est pater pueri?' Danae
     respondit: 'pater pueri est Iuppiter, rex deorum.'
5   Acrisius et matrem et filium punire constituit.

peperit = gave birth to

(35)

2   (a) pueri (line 1). In which case is this noun?   (1)

     (b) erat (line 2). Give the 1st person singular of the
         present tense of this verb.   (1)

     (c) Give an example from the passage of an infinitive.   (1)

     (d) matrem (line 5). Give the gender of this noun.   (1)

3   Using the vocabulary given below, translate the following sentences into Latin:

     (a) The small boys are afraid.   (3)

     (b) The angry son was shouting.   (3)

small	parvus, -a, -um
boy	puer, pueri, m.
I am afraid	timeo, -ere (2)
angry	iratus, -a, -um
son	filius, -i, m.
I shout	clamo, -are (1)

Total: 45

Test 5: The story of Perseus (5)

1 Translate the following passage into good English:

Acrisius thinks he has disposed of Danae and Perseus

1 Acrisius Danaen et Perseum in magna cista clausit.
deinde servos cistam ad litus portare et in mare
iacere iussit. Danae et Perseus perterriti erant.
undas timebant. tandem undae cistam ad insulam
5 pepulerunt. ibi senex, Dictys nomine, eos invenit
et servavit.

Danaen = the accusative case of Danae (Greek form)
cista, -ae, f. = chest
claudo, -ere, clausum (3) = I shut
litus, litoris, n. = shore, beach
mare, maris, n. = sea
pello, -ere, pepuli (3) = I drive
invenio, -ire, inveni (4) = I find
servo, -are, -avi (1) = I save

(40)

2 (a) Give an example from the passage of a conjunction. (1)

(b) iussit (line 3). Give the 1st person singular of the present tense of this verb. (1)

(c) erant (line 3). Give the number of this verb. (1)

(d) nomine (line 5). In which case is this noun? (1)

3 Using the vocabulary given below, translate the following sentences into Latin:

(a) The slave was afraid of the waves. (3)

(b) I like the big island. (3)

slave	servus, -i, m.
I am afraid	timeo, -ere (2)
wave	unda, -ae, f.
I like	amo, -are (1)
big	magnus, -a, -um
island	insula, -ae, f.

Total: 50

1 Translate the following passage into good English:

King Polydectes takes a fancy to Danae

1 Danae et Perseus in insula laeti diu habitabant. Perseus iuvenis iam erat et mater eius femina <u>adhuc</u> pulchra erat. rex insulae, Polydectes nomine, ubi <u>Danaen</u> conspexit, eam statim amavit et <u>ducere</u>
5 cupiebat. Perseus tamen Polydectem non amabat. ei clamavit: 'numquam matrem meam <u>duces</u>.'

adhuc = still
Danaen = the accusative case of Danae (Greek form)
duco, -ere, duxi (3) = I marry

(40)

2 (a) Give an example from the passage of an adverb. (1)

(b) habitabant (line 1). Give the tense of this verb. (1)

(c) erat (line 2). Give the number of this verb. (1)

(d) conspexit (line 4). Give the 1st person singular of the present tense of this verb. (1)

3 Using the vocabulary below, translate the following sentences into Latin:

(a) The woman liked the island. (3)

(b) The good women were shouting. (3)

woman	femina, -ae, f.
I like	amo, -are (1)
island	insula, -ae, f.
good	bonus, -a, -um
I shout	clamo, -are, (1)

Total: 50

Test 7: The story of Perseus (7)

1   Translate the following passage into good English:

King Polydectes issues a challenge to Perseus

1   Perseus Polydectem non amabat. Polydectes
    Perseum non amabat. Perseus fortis erat sed iuvenis.
    regi igitur, 'Polydectes,' inquit, 'ego te non timeo.
    ego vir fortis sum.' 'si vir fortis es,' respondit   si = if
5   Polydectes, 'Medusam neca, deinde caput eius   caput, capitis, n. = head
    ad me fer!'   fer! = bring!

                                                                    (40)

2   (a) erat (line 2). Give the 1st person singular of the present
        tense of this verb.   (1)

    (b) regi (line 3). In which case is this noun?   (1)

    (c) timeo (line 3). Give the person of this verb.   (1)

    (d) Give an example from the passage of a personal pronoun.   (1)

3   Using the vocabulary given below, translate the following sentences into Latin:

    (a) Perseus kills Medusa.   (3)

    (b) The boy was afraid of the girl.   (3)

Perseus	Perseus, i, m.
I kill	neco, -are (1)
Medusa	Medusa, ae, f.
boy	puer, pueri, m.
I am afraid of	timeo, -ere (2)
girl	puella, -ae, f.

Total: 50

1 Translate the following passage into good English:

Perseus receives help from the gods

1 haec verba Polydectis Perseum terruerunt. hic,
 quamquam iuvenis fortis erat, Medusam timebat. dei
 tamen deaeque auxilium Perseo dederunt. gladium
 novum et scutum <u>politum</u> ei dederunt. Perseus, ubi   politus, -a, -um =
5 haec arma accepit, iam laetus erat. non iam Medusam   polished
 timebat. ab insula navigavit et ad Medusam iter fecit.

(45)

2 (a) ei (line 4). Give the nominative masculine singular of this pronoun. (1)

 (b) dederunt (line 4). Give the 1st person singular of the present tense
 of this verb. (1)

 (c) insula (line 6). In which case is this noun? Why is this case used? (2)

3 Using the vocabulary given below, translate the following sentences into Latin:

 (a) The boys have new swords. (4)

 (b) We frighten the goddess. (2)

boy	puer, pueri, m.
I have	habeo, -ere (2)
new	novus, -a, -um
sword	gladius, -i, m.
I frighten	terreo, -ere (2)
goddess	dea, -ae, f.

Total: 55

Test 9: The story of Perseus (9)

1   Translate the following passage into good English:

Perseus kills Medusa

1   iter longum erat. Perseus tamen post multa pericula
    ad terram, ubi Medusa habitabat, tandem advenit.
    cum Medusa fortiter pugnavit et auxilio deorum
    eam occidit. ubi hoc fecit, <u>caput</u> eius <u>abscidit</u> et ad
5   insulam rediit.

caput, capitis, n. = head
abscido, -ere, abscidi
(3) = I cut off

(35)

2   (a) iter (line 1). Give the gender of this noun.   (1)

    (b) terram (line 2). In which case is this noun?   (1)

    (c) Give an example from the passage of an adverb.   (1)

    (d) fecit (line 4). Give the 1st person singular of the present
        tense of this verb.   (1)

3   Using the vocabulary given below, translate the following sentences into Latin:

    (a) They do not fear dangers.   (3)

    (b) The god liked the island.   (3)

not	non
I fear	timeo, -ere (2)
danger	periculum, -i, n.
god	deus, -i, m.
I like	amo, -are (1)
island	insula, -ae, f.

Total: 45

Test 10: The story of Perseus (10)

1 Translate the following passage into good English:

Perseus saves Andromeda

1 Perseus Medusam occiderat. ad Graeciam iam
   redibat et caput Medusae in sacco portabat. in
   itinere puellam pulchram conspexit. nomen huius
   puellae Andromeda erat. illa perterrita erat, quod
5 monstrum eam petebat. Perseus tamen eam
   servavit. caput Medusae monstro ostendit et in
   saxum id mutavit.

Graecia, -ae, f. =
Greece
caput, capitis, n. =
head
saccus, -i, m. = bag
monstrum, -i, n. =
monster
peto, -ere, petivi (3) =
I attack
saxum, -i, n. = rock

(50)

2 (a) occiderat (line 1). Give the tense of this verb.   (1)

   (b) Give an example from the passage of a preposition.   (1)

   (c) Medusae (line 2). In which case is this noun?   (1)

   (d) conspexit (line 3). Give the 1st person singular of the
       present tense of this verb.   (1)

3 Using the vocabulary given below, translate the following sentences into Latin:

   (a) Perseus sees Medusa.   (3)

   (b) We were carrying the frightened girl.   (3)

Perseus	Perseus, -i, m.
I see	video, -ere (2)
Medusa	Medusa, -ae, f.
I carry	porto, -are (1)
frightened	perterritus, -a, -um
girl	puella, -ae, f.

Total: 50

Test 11: The story of Perseus (11)

1 Translate the following passage into good English:

Perseus surprises Polydectes

1 Perseus, ubi Andromedam servavit, ad <u>Graeciam</u>
   rediit. Polydectes, ubi Perseum vidit, iratus erat.
   'quid hic facis?' Perseo clamavit. 'num <u>caput</u>
   Medusae habes?' Perseus respondit: 'Medusam
5 occidi et <u>caput</u> eius hic habeo. specta!' <u>caput</u>
   Medusae Perseus ostendit. Polydectes <u>caput</u>
   spectavit et in <u>saxum</u> statim <u>mutatus est</u>.

Graecia, -ae, f. = Greece

caput, capitis, n. = head

saxum, -i, n. = rock
mutatus est = (he) was turned

(45)

2 (a) Graeciam (line 1). In which case is this noun? (1)

   (b) rediit (line 2). Give the 1st person singular of the
       present tense of this verb. (1)

   (c) facis (line 3). Give the person of this verb. (1)

   (d) Give an example from the passage of an adverb. (1)

3 Using the vocabulary given below, translate the following sentences into Latin:

   (a) Andromeda sees the islands. (3)

   (b) Perseus was looking at Medusa. (3)

Andromeda	Andromeda, -ae, f.
I see	video, -ere (2)
island	insula, -ae, f.
Perseus	Perseus, -i, m.
I look at	specto, -are (1)
Medusa	Medusa, -ae, f.

Total: 55

1 Translate the following passage into good English:

The oracle is fulfilled at the city of Larissa

1 Perseus Polydectem occiderat. Danae, mater pulchra
   Persei, tuta iam erat. diu Perseus et Danae laetissimi
   habitabant. olim Perseus ad urbem Larissam iter fecit.
   ibi certamina athletica habebantur. Perseus discum
5 iecit. discus forte spectatorem icit et necavit. hic
   spectator Acrisius erat. dei vera dixerant: Perseus
   avum suum occiderat.

certamina athletica
habebantur =
athletics contests were
being held
discus, -i, m. = discus
spectator, -oris, m. =
spectator
icit = (it) struck
vera = the truth
avus, -i, m. =
grandfather

(44)

2 (a) urbem (line 3). In which case is this noun?   (1)

   (b) iecit (line 5). Give the 1st person singular of the present
       tense of this verb.   (1)

   (c) necavit (line 5). Give the number of this verb.   (1)

   (d) Give an example from the passage of a superlative adjective.   (1)

3 Using the vocabulary given below, translate the following sentences into Latin:

   (a) Perseus kills the grandfather.   (4)

   (b) The happy gods were watching.   (3)

Perseus	Perseus, -i, m.
I kill	neco, -are (1)
grandfather	avus, -i, m.
happy	laetus, -a, -um
god	deus, -i, m.
I watch	specto, -are (1)

Total: 55